Stanley Kubrick's A Clockwork Orange

Based on the novel by Anthony Burgess

BALLANTINE BOOKS • NEW YORK • An INTEXT Publisher

"Singin' In The Rain"
Lyrics: Arthur Freed, Music: Nacio Herb Brown
Copyright 1929, Metro-Goldwyn-Mayer
Renewed 1957 Robbins Music Corporation.
Reprinted by permission.

First Printing: July, 1972
Printed in the United States of America

Cover design by Philip Castle. Copyright 1971 by Warner
Bros. Productions Limited.

BALLANTINE BOOKS, INC.
101 Fifth Avenue, New York, N.Y. 10003

May 22, 1972

"I have always wondered if there might be a more meaningful way to present a book about a film. To make, as it were, a complete, graphic representation of the film, cut by cut, with the dialogue printed in the proper place in relation to the cuts, so that within the limits of still-photographs and words, an accurate (and I hope interesting) record of a film might be available to anyone who had a bit more curiosity than just knowing what happened in the last reel. This book represents that attempt. If there are inaccuracies then they have escaped the endless checking and re-checking of myself and my assistants, Andros Epaminondas and Margaret Adams."

Stanley Kubrick

Reel 1

WARNER BROS.

A KINNEY COMPANY

Presents

A
STANLEY KUBRICK
PRODUCTION

A CLOCKWORK ORANGE

Night Interior. Korova Milkbar.

Alex: *(Voice Over)* **There was me, that is Alex, and my three droogs, that is Pete, Georgie and Dim and we sat in the Korova milkbar trying to make up our rassoodocks what to do with the evening. The Korova milkbar sold milk-plus, milk plus vellocet or synthemesc or drencrom, which is what we were drinking. This would sharpen you up and make you ready for a bit of the old ultra-violence.**

Night Exterior. Pedestrian Underpass.

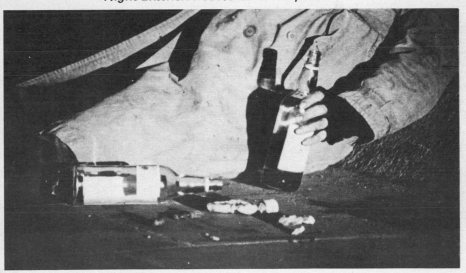

Tramp: *In Dublin's fair city, where the girls are so pretty, I first set my eyes on sweet Molly Malone,*
As she wheeled her wheelbarrow
Through streets broad and narrow

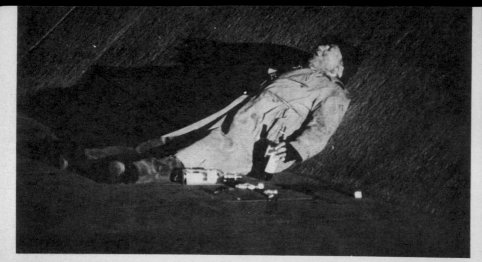

Crying cockles and mussels alive alive O . . . .

Alex: *(Voice Over)* **One thing I could never stand was to see a filthy, dirty old drunkie,**

howling away at the filthy songs of his fathers and going blerp, blerp in between, as it might be a filthy old orchestra in his stinking rotten guts. I could never stand to see anyone like that, whatever his age might be, but more especially when he was real old like this one was.

The boys stop and applaud him.

Tramp: Can you spare some cutter, me brothers?

Alex rams his stick into the tramp's stomach.

Go on, do me in, you bastard cowards.
I don't want to live anyway . . . not in a stinking world like this.

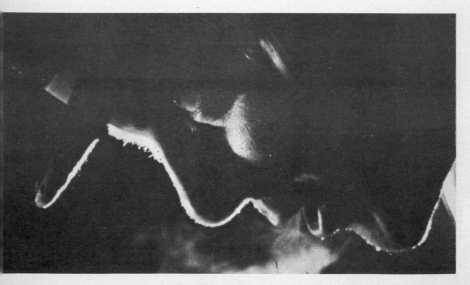

Alex: Oh . . . and what's so stinking about it?

Tramp: It's a stinking world because there's no law and order any more. It's a stinking world because it lets the young get onto the old, like you done. Oh . . . it's no world for an old man any longer. What sort of a world is it at all? Men on the moon, and men spinning around the earth, and there's not no attention paid to earthly law and order no more.

Oh dear land, I fought for thee and brought...

Night Interior. Derelict Casino.

Billyboy: Right, get her clothes off.
Alex: *(Voice Over)* It was around by the
derelict casino that we came across
Billyboy and his four droogs. They were
getting ready to perform a little of the old
in-out, in-out on a weepy young
devotchka they had there.

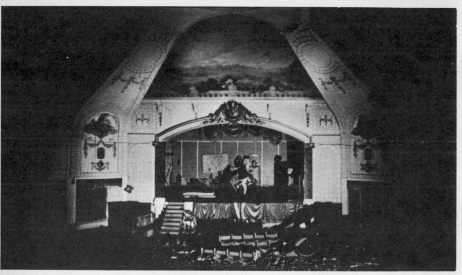

Alex: Ho, Ho, Ho. Well, if it isn't

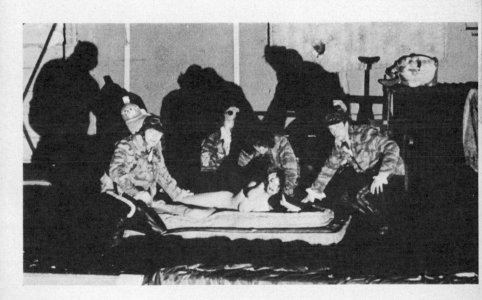

fat, stinking Billygoat Billyboy in poison.

How art thou, thou globby bottle of cheap,
stinking chip oil ?

Come and get one in the yarbles, if you have any yarbles, you eunuch jelly thou.

Billyboy: Let's get 'em, boys.

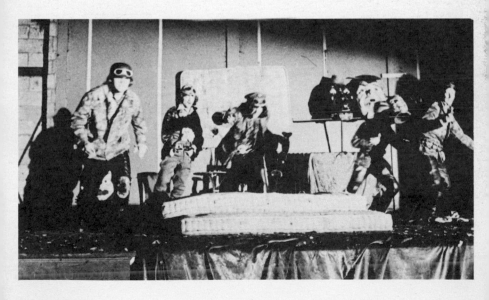

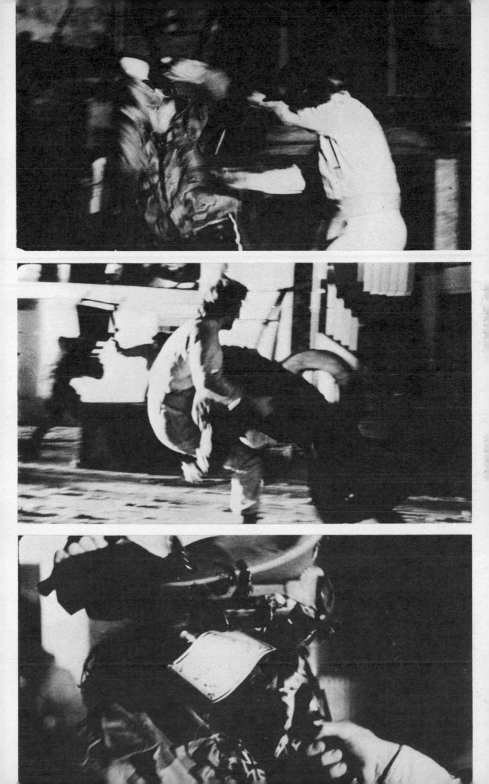

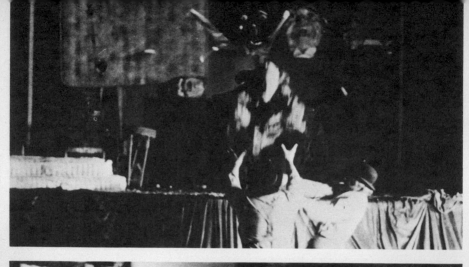

Police sirens.

Alex: The Police . . . come on, let's go . . . .

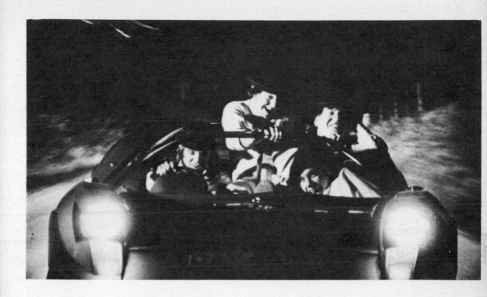

Night. Interior. Car.

Alex: *(Voice Over)* **The Durango-95 purred away real horrorshow – a nice, warm vibraty feeling all through your guttiwuts. Soon, it was trees and dark, my brothers, with real country dark.**

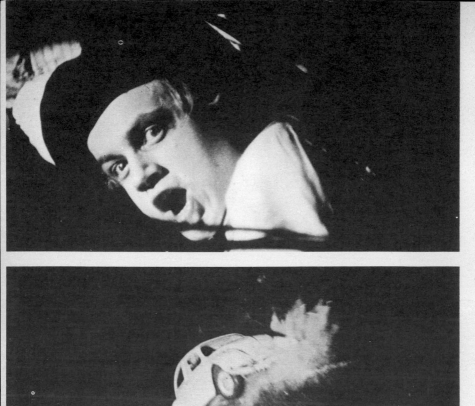

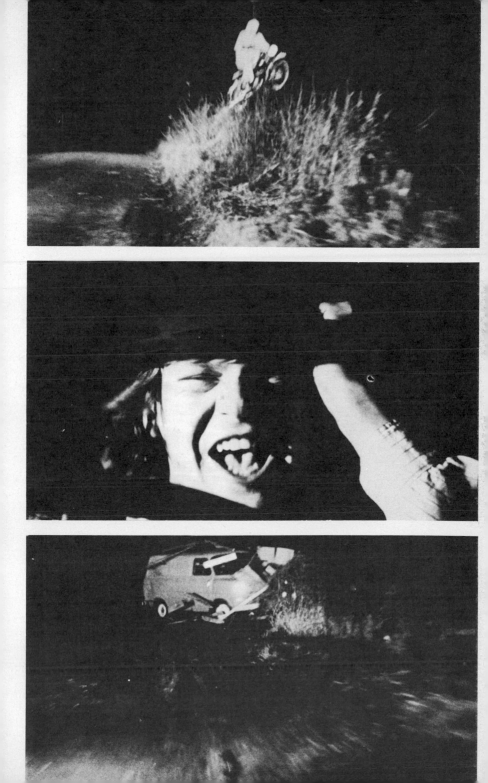

We fillied around for a while with other travellers of the night, playing hogs of the road. Then we headed west, what we were after now was the old surprise visit. That was a real kick and good for laughs and lashings of the old ultra-violence.

Reel 2

Night Interior. "Home".

Door chime rings .

Mr. Alexander: Who on earth could that be?

Mrs. Alexander: I'll go and see.

Yes? Who is it?

Alex: Excuse me, missus . . . can you please help us? There's been a terrible accident. My friend's in the middle of the road bleeding to death. Can I please use your telephone for an ambulance?

Mrs. Alexander: I'm sorry but we don't have a telephone. You'll have to go somewhere else.

Alex: But, missus, it's a matter of life and death.

Mr. Alexander: Who is it, dear?

Mrs. Alexander: There's a young man here. He says there's been an accident. He wants to use the telephone.

Mr. Alexander: Well, I suppose you'd better let him in.

She unlatches the door.

Mrs. Alexander: Well, wait a minute, will you?

I'm sorry, but we don't usually let strangers in in the middle . . .

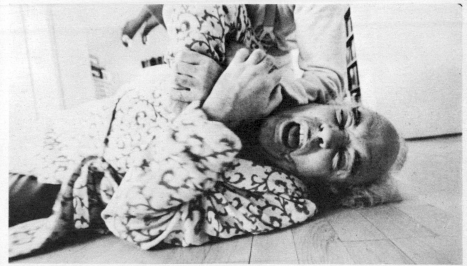

Alex: Right, Pete. Check the rest of the house. Dim...

I'm singin' in the rain . . .
Just singin' in the rain . .
What a glorious feeling . .
I'm happy again . .
I'm laughing at clouds . .

So dark up above . .
The sun's in my heart
And I'm ready for love.

Let the stormy clouds chase
Everyone from the place.
Come on with the rain,

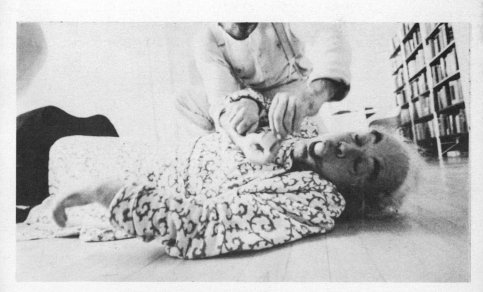

I've a smile on my face.
I'll walk down the lane,

With a happy refrain
And I'm singin', just singin'
in the rain.

Doobidoob, dooby, dooby,
Doobidoob, dooby, dooby,
Doobidoob, dooby, dooby
Doo

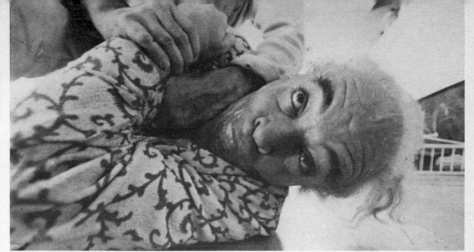

Alex begins snipping off Mrs. Alexander's pyjama suit.

> *I'm singin' in the rain,*
>
> **Dim:** *(laughing moronically) He's singing in the rain.*
> **Alex:** *Just singin' in the rain.*
> **Dim:** *In the rain.*
> **Alex:** *What a glorious feeling.*
> **Dim:** *Feeling.*
> **Alex:** *And, I'm happy again.*

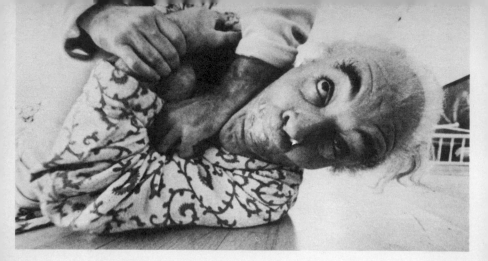

I'm laughing at clouds
Dim: *At clouds.*

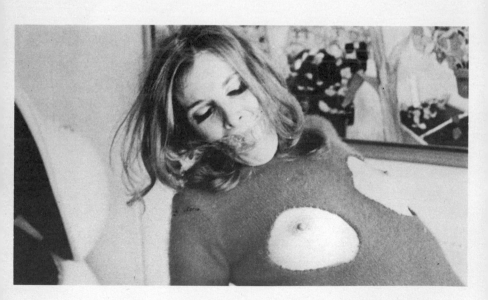

Alex: *So dark up above*
The sun's in my heart.
Dim: *The sun's in my heart.*

Alex: *And I'm ready for love.*
Dim: *Ready for love.*
Alex: *Let the stormy clouds chase.*

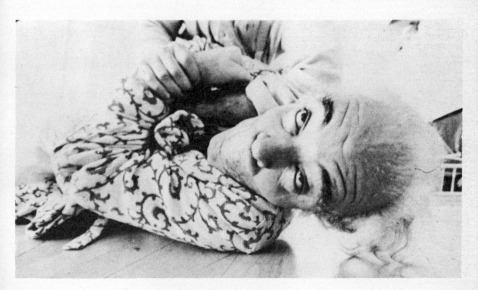

Dim: *Ready for love.*

Alex: *Everyone from the place.*
Come on with the rain
I've a smile on my face.
Dim: *Ready for love.*
Alex: *I'll walk down the lane*
With a happy refrain

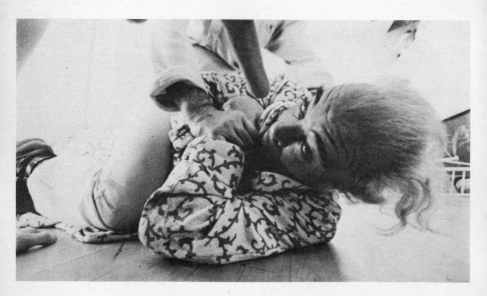

I am singin', just singing
In the rain.

Viddy well, little brother. Viddy well.

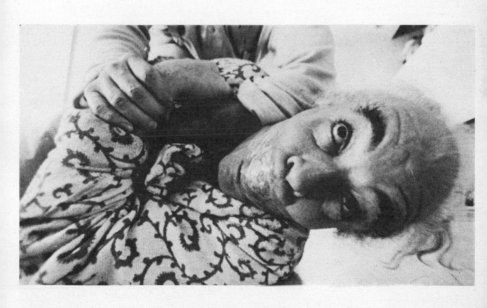

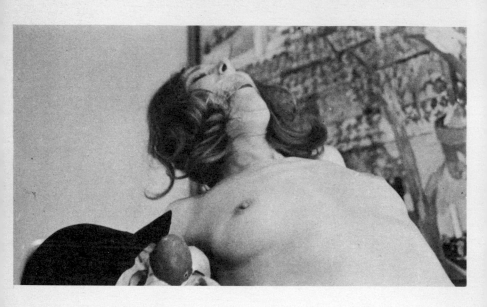

Night Interior. Korova Milkbar.

The gang enters

Alex: *(Voice Over)* We were all feeling a bit shagged and fagged and fashed, it having been an evening of some small energy expenditure, O my brothers. So we got rid of the auto and stopped off at the Korova for a nightcap.

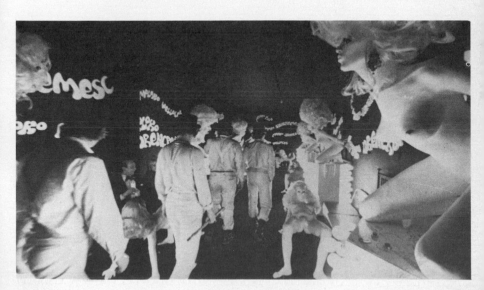

Dim speaks to milk-machine figure

Dim : Hello, Lucy, had a busy night ?
We've been working hard, too. Pardon me,
Luce.

Alex : *(Voice Over)* There were some
sophistos from the TV studios around the
corner, laughing and govoreeting. The
devotchka was smecking away and not
caring about the wicked world one bit.
Then the disc on the stereo twanged off
and out, and in the short silence before
the next one came on, she suddenly came
with a burst of singing .

*The girl sings a short section from Beethoven's
Ninth Symphony.*

Alex: *(Voice Over)* **It was like for a
moment, O my brothers, some great
bird had flown into the milkbar and I felt
all the malenky little hairs on my plott
standing endwise and the shivers crawling
up like slow malenky lizards and then
down again.**

**Because I knew what she sang.
It was a bit from the glorious Ninth,
by Ludwig van.**

Dim blows a raspberry at singer.

Alex smashes Dim across the legs with his stick.

Dim: What did you do that for?

Alex: For being a bastard with no manners and not a dook of an idea how to comport yourself publicwise, O my brother.

Dim: I don't like you should do what you done. And I'm not your brother no more and wouldn't want to be.

Alex: Watch that . . . Do watch that, O Dim, if to continue to be on live thou dost wish.

Dim: Yarbles, great bolshy yarblockos to you.

I'll meet you with chain or nozh or britva any time. Not having you aiming tolchocks at me reasonless,

it stands to reason I won't have it.

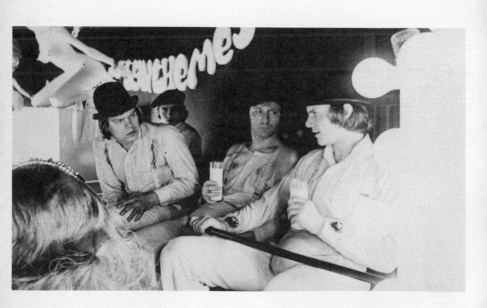

Alex: A nozh scrap any time you say.

Dim slowly backs down.

Dim: Doobidoob.

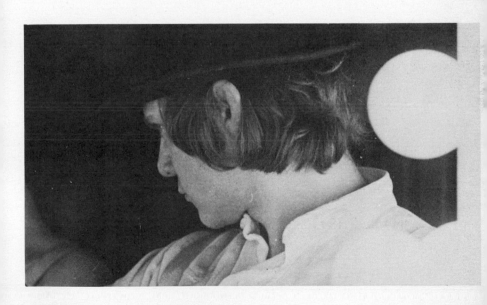

A bit tired maybe.

Best not to say more. Bedways is rightways
now, so best we go homeways and get a bit of
spatchka. Righty, right?
Pete/Georgie: Righty, right.
Alex: Right, right.

Reel 3

Night Exterior. Flatblock.

Alex: *(Voice Over)* **Where I lived was with my dadda and mum in municipal flatblock 18a Linear North.**

Night Interior. Flatblock Lobby.

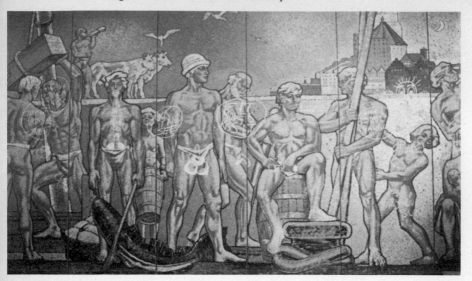

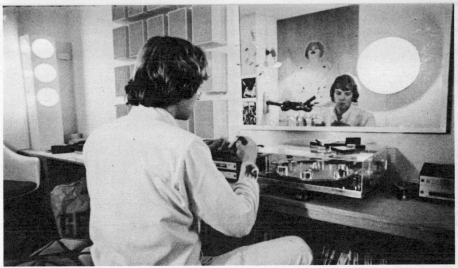

Alex: *(Voice Over)* It had been a wonderful evening and what I needed now to give it the perfect ending was a bit of the old Ludwig van.

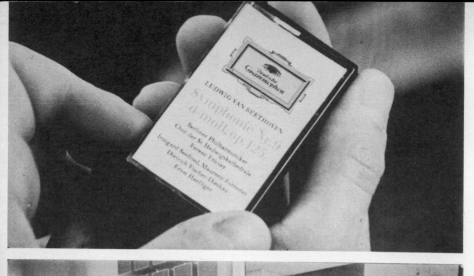

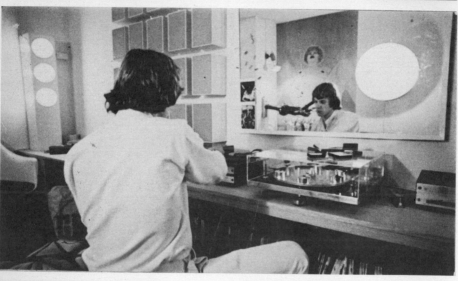

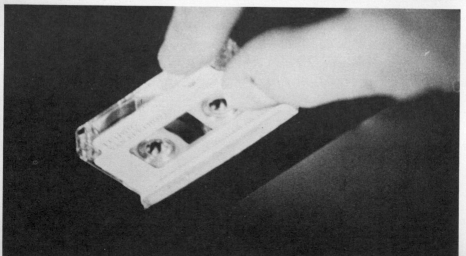

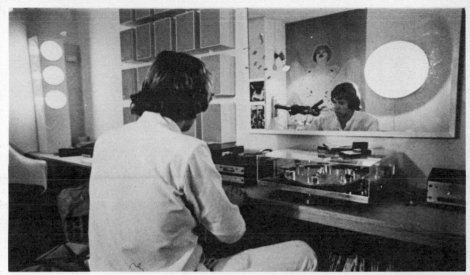

Beethoven's Ninth fills the room

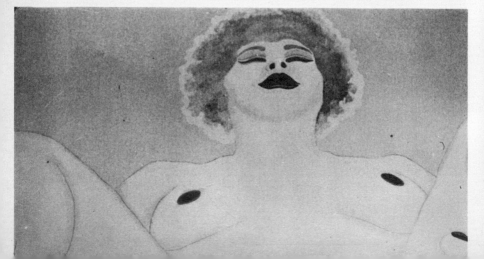

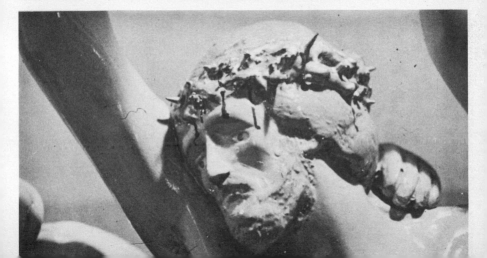

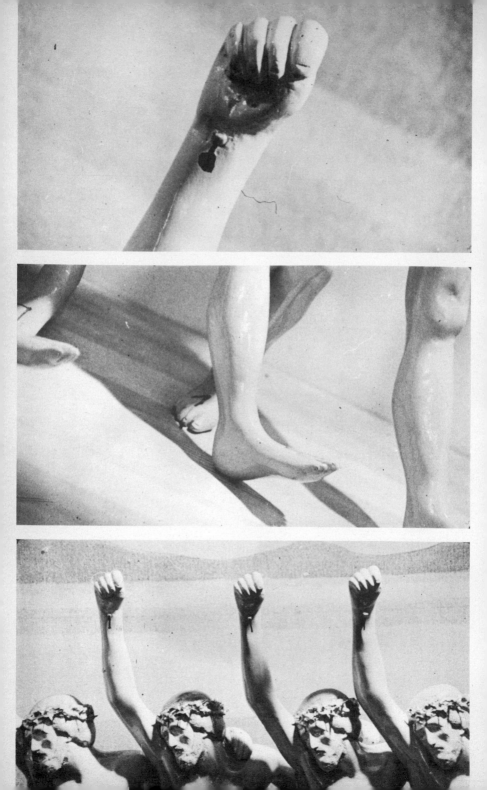

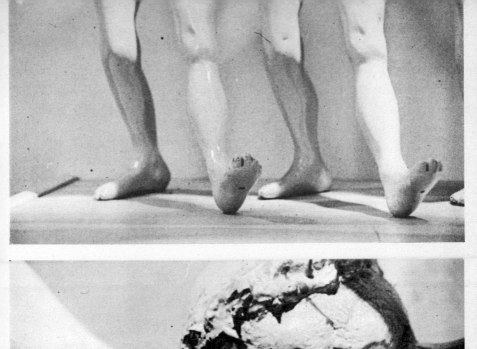

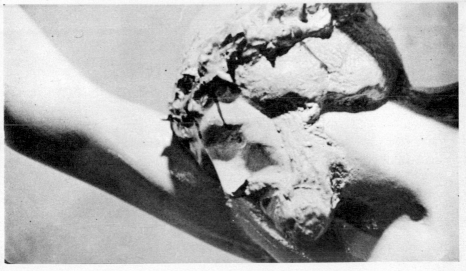

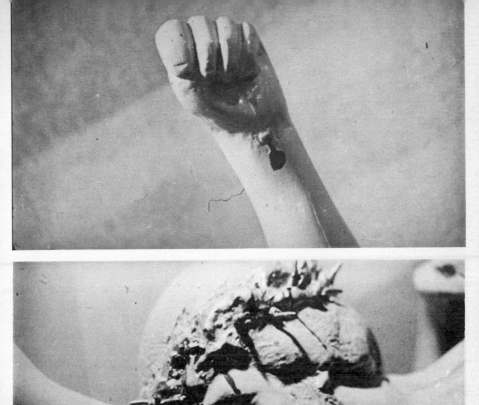
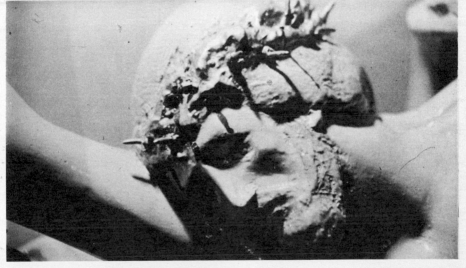

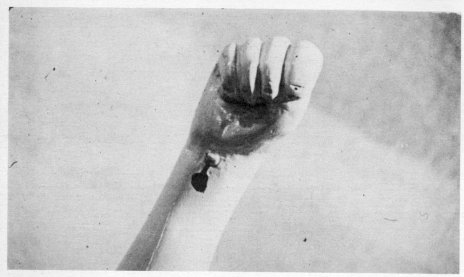

Oh, bliss . . . bliss and heaven. Oh, it was
gorgeousness and gorgeosity made flesh.
It was like a bird of rarest spun heaven metal,
or like silvery wine flowing in a space ship,
gravity all nonsense now.

As I slooshied I knew such lovely pictures.

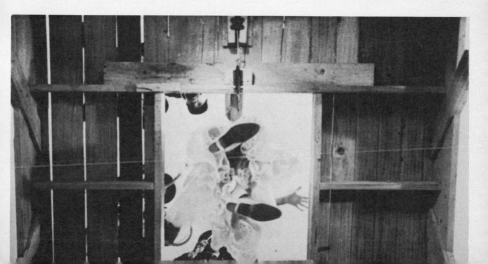

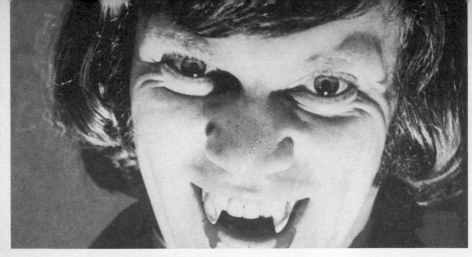

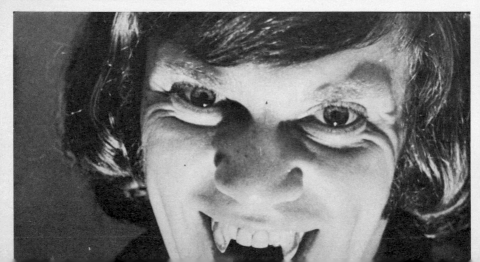

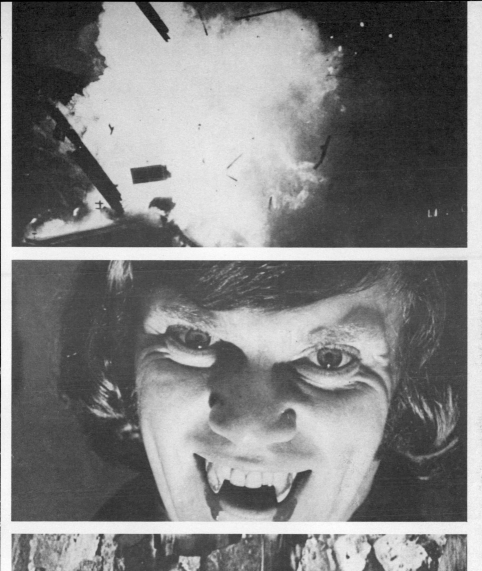

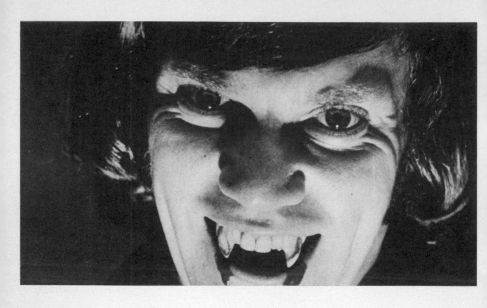

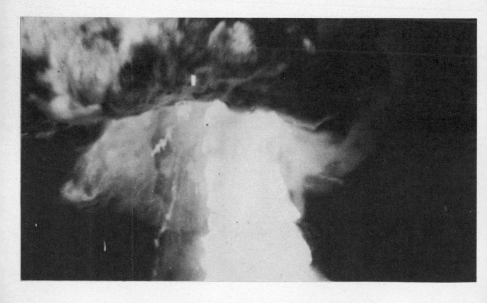

Day Interior. Alex's Flat.
Em knocks on his door.

Em: Alex, Alex . . . Alex . . . Alex . . .

Alex: What do you want?
Em: It's past eight, Alex. You don't want to be late for school, son.
Alex: Bit of a pain in the gulliver, Mum. Leave us be and I'll try and sleep it off. And then I'll be as right as dodgers for this after.

Em: But you've not been to school all week, son.

Alex: Got to rest, Mum. Got to get fit. Otherwise I'm liable to miss a lot more school.
Em: All right, I'll put your breakfast in the oven. I've got to be off myself now.
Alex: All right, Mum. Have a nice day at the factory.

Day. Interior. Kitchen.
Enter Em.

Em: He's not feeling too good again this morning, Dad.

Pee: Yes, yes, I heard. Do you know what time he got in last night?

Em: No, I don't, love. I'd taken my sleepers.

Pee: I wonder . . . where exactly is it he goes to work of evenings?

Em: Well, like he says, it's mostly odd things he does . . . helping like . . . here and there as it might be.

Alex: Hi hi hi, Mr. Deltoid. Funny surprise seeing you here.

Deltoid: Well, Alex boy, awake at last, yes?
I met your mother on the way to work, yes,
she gave me the key. She said something about
a pain somewhere, hence not at school, yes?

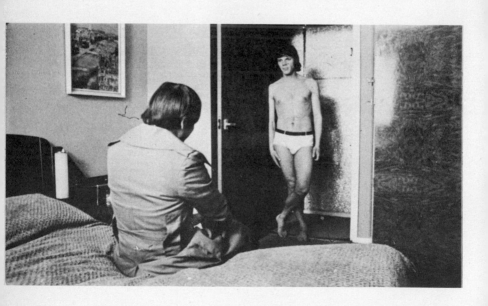

Alex: A rather intolerable pain in the head,
brother, sir. I think it should be clear by this
afterlunch.

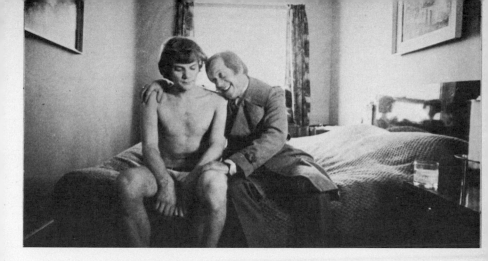

Deltoid: Or certainly by this evening, yes? The evening's the great time, isn't it, Alex boy, hmm?

Alex: A cup of the old chai, sir?

Deltoid: No time, no time, yes? Sit, sit, sit.

Alex sits next to Deltoid.

Alex: To what do I owe this extreme pleasure, sir? Anything wrong, sir?

Deltoid: Wrong? Why should you think of anything being wrong? Have you been doing something you shouldn't, yes?

Alex: Just a manner of speech, sir.

Deltoid: Yes, well, it is just a manner of speech from your Post Corrective Adviser to you that you watch out, little Alex. Because next time it's not going to be the corrective school any more. Next time, it's going to be the barry place and all my work ruined. If you've no respect for your horrible self, you at least might have some for me who's sweated over you. A big black mark, I tell you, for every one we don't reclaim. A confession of failure for every one of you who ends up in the stripy hole.

Alex: I've been doing nothing I shouldn't, sir. The millicents have nothing on me, brother, sir, I mean.

Deltoid: Cut out all this clever talk about millicents. Just because the police haven't picked you up lately doesn't, as you very well know, mean that you've not been up to some nastiness. There was a bit of a nastiness last night, yes. Some very extreme nastiness, yes. A few of a certain Billyboy's friends were ambulanced off late, yes? Your name was mentioned, the word has got thru to me by the usual channels. Certain friends of yours were named also. Oh, nobody can prove anything about anybody as usual, but I'm warning you, little Alex, being a good friend to you as always, the one man in this sore and sick community who wants to save you from yourself.

Deltoid makes a grab for Alex's crotch.

Alex gets up from the bed.

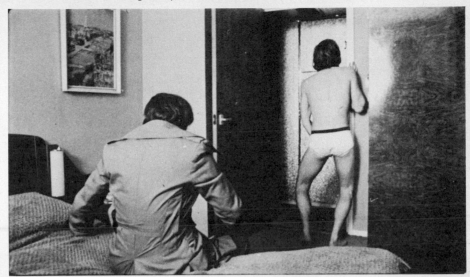

What gets into you all? We study the problem.
We've been studying it for damn well near a
century, yes, but we get no further with our
studies. You've got a good home here, good
loving parents, you've got not too bad of a brain.
Is it some devil that crawls inside of you?
Alex: Nobody's got anything on me, brother,
sir. I've been out of the rookers of the millicents
for a long time now.

Deltoid: That's just what worries me. A bit too long to be safe. You're about due now by my reckoning. That's why I'm warning you, little Alex, to keep your handsome young proboscis out of the dirt. Do I make myself clear ?

Alex: As an unmuddied lake, sir. As clear as an azure sky of deepest summer. You can rely on me, sir.

Reel 4

Day. Interior. Music Bootick.

Alex: Excuse me, brother. I ordered this two weeks ago. Can you see if it's arrived yet, please?

Clerk: Just a minute.

Two girls licking phallic ice sticks.

Alex: Pardon me, ladies.

Enjoying that are you my darling? Bit cold and pointless isn't it, my lovely? What's happened to yours, my little sister?

Marty: Who you getten, bratty? Goggly Gogol? Johnny Zhivago? The Heaven Seventeen?

Alex: What you got back home, little sister, to play your fuzzy warbles on? I bet you got little save pitiful portable picnic players. Come with uncle and hear all proper. Hear angel trumpets and devil trombones. You are invited.

Alex's room.

High speed Orgy. Camera shooting at 2 frames per second.

Day. Interior. Flatblock Lobby.

Alex: Hi hi hi there.

All three: Well, hello.

Dim: He are here! He have arrived! Hooray!

Alex: Welly, welly, welly, welly, welly, welly, well. To what do I owe the extreme pleasure of this surprising visit?

Georgie: We got worried.

There we were awaiting and drinking away at the old knify moloko and you had not turned up, and we thought you might have been like offended by something or other, so round we come to your abode.

Alex: Appy polly loggies. I had something of
a pain in the gulliver so had to sleep. I was not
awakened when I gave orders for wakening.

Dim: Sorry about the pain. Using the gulliver
too much like, maybe ?

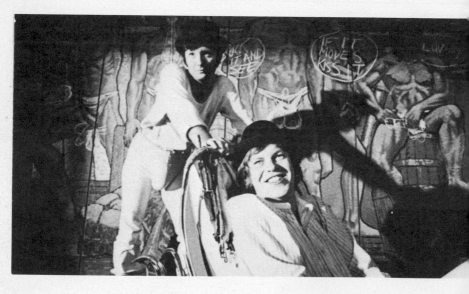

Giving orders and discipline and such perhaps ?

Sure the pain has gone ?
You sure you'd not be happier back in bed ?

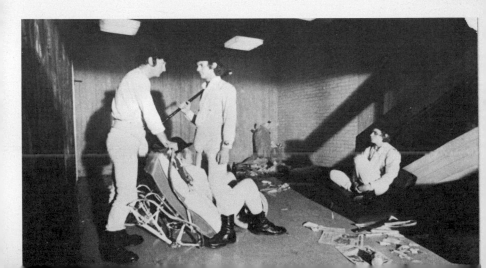

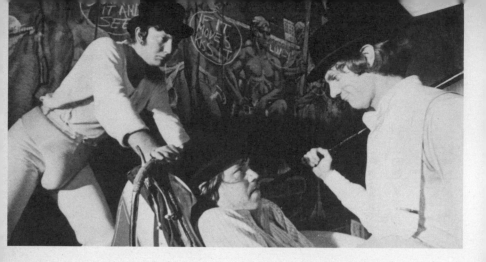

Alex: Let's get things nice and sparkling clear. This sarcasm, if I may call it such, does not become you, O my little brothers. As I am your droog and leader, I am entitled to know what goes on, eh? Now then, Dim, what does that great big horsy gape of a grin portend?
Georgie: All right, no more picking on Dim, brother. That's part of the new way.
Alex: New way? What's this about a new way? There's been some very large talk behind my sleeping back, and no error.

Georgie: Well, if you must have it, have it then. We go around, shop crasting and the like, coming out with a pitiful rookerful of money each.

Dim: Pitiful rookerful . . .

Georgie: And there's Will the English, in the Muscleman coffee mesto, saying he can fence anything that any malchick tries to crast.

The shiny stuff . . . the ice . . . the big, big, big money is available, is what Will the English says.

Dim: Big, big money.

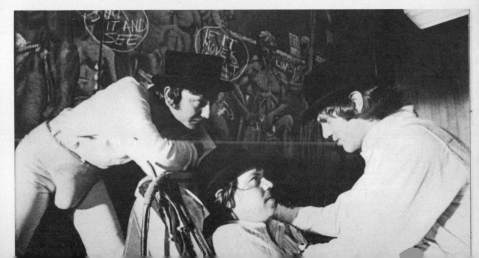

Alex: And what will you do with the big, big, big money ? Have you not everything you need ? If you need a motor car, you pluck it from the trees. If you need pretty polly, you take it.
Georgie: Brother, you think and talk sometimes like a little child.
Dim: Little child, yes . . .
Georgie: Tonight, we pull a mansize crast.

Dim: Tonight's a mansize crast.
Alex: Good. Real horrorshow. Initiative comes to thems that wait.

I've taught you much, my little droogies. Now tell me what you have in mind, Georgie boy.

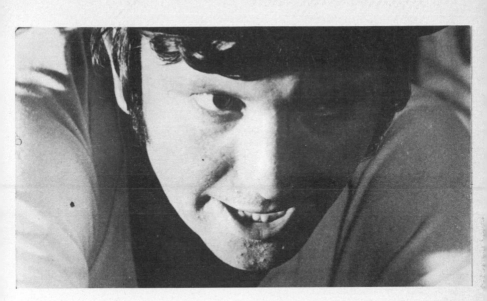

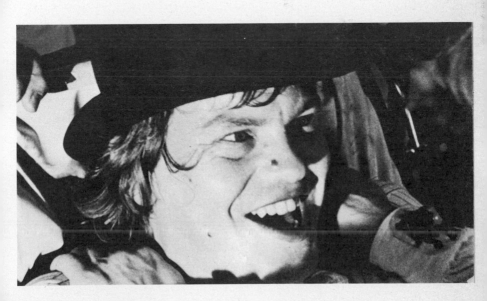

Georgie: Oh, the old moloko- plus first, would you not say?

Dim: Moloko-plus.

Georgie: Something to sharpen us up.

Dim: Get some of that down you . . . some of the moloko-plus.

Georgie: But you especially, we have the start.

Dim: Yea, you've got to have some first because we've got a start on you. Yea . . . moloko-plus, yea . . . (laughs moronically)

Reel 5

Day. Exterior. Flatblock Marina.

Alex: *(Voice Over)* As we walked along the flatblock marina, I was calm on the outside but thinking all the time. So now it was to be Georgie the General, saying what we should do, and what not to do, and Dim as his mindless, grinning bulldog. But, suddenly, I viddied that thinking was for the gloopy ones, and that the oomny ones used like inspiration and what Bog sends. For now it was lovely music that came to my aid. There was a window open, with a stereo on, and I viddied right at once what to do.

In slow motion—

Alex attacks the Droogs.

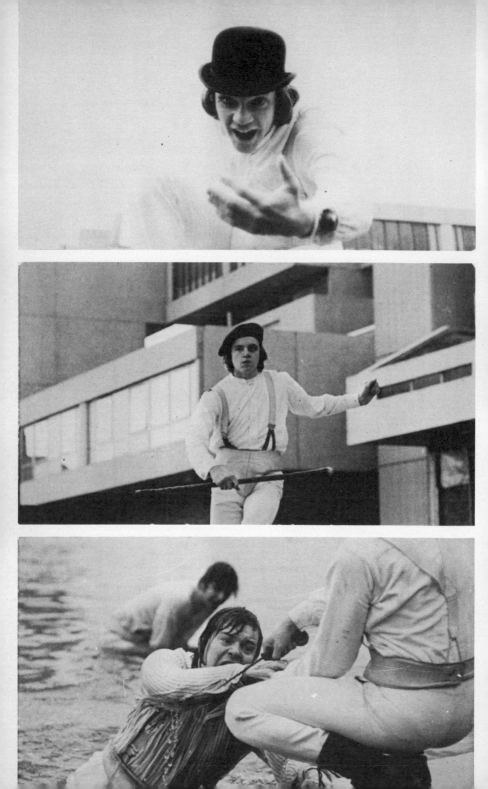

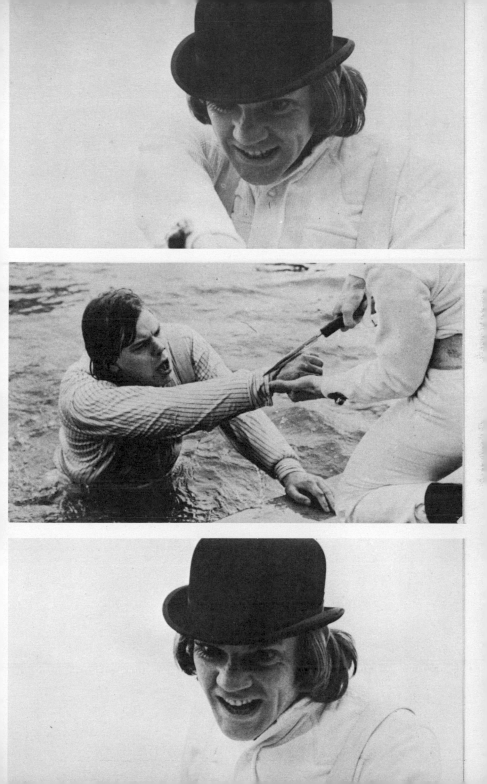

Night. Interior. Duke of New York Pub. The boys are seated at a table.

Alex: *(Voice Over)* I had not cut into any of Dim's main cables and so, with the help of a clean tashtook, the red, red krovvy soon stopped, and it did not take long to quieten the two wounded soldiers, down in the snug of the Duke of New York.

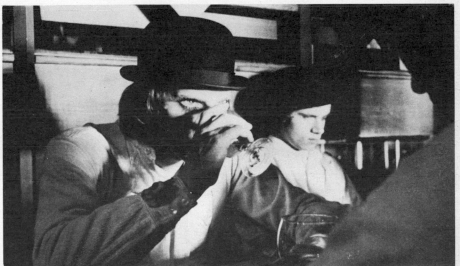

Now they knew who was Master and Leader. Sheep, thought I, but a real leader knows always when like to give and show generous to his unders.
Alex: Well, now we're back to where we were, yes? Just like before and all forgotten?

Right, right, right?
Pete: Right.

Dim: Right.
Georgie: Right.

Alex: Well, Georgie, boy. This idea of yours
for tonight, tell us all about it then.
Georgie: Not tonight. Not this nochy.
Alex: Come, come, come, Georgie boy.
You're a big strong chelloveck like us all.
We're not little children are we, Georgie boy?
What then didst thou in thy mind have?

Night. Interior. The Health Farm.

Georgie : It's this Health Farm. A bit out of the town. Isolated.
It's owned by this like very rich ptitsa who lives there with her cats. The place is shut down for a week, and she's completely on her own, and it's full up with like gold and silver, and like jewels.
Alex : Tell me more, Georgie boy. Tell me more.
Some loud knocks on the door.

Catlady: Oh, shit.
She unravels herself and goes to the door.

Catlady: Who's there?
Alex: Excuse me, missus. Can you please help? There's been a terrible accident. Can I please use your telephone for an ambulance?
Catlady: I'm frightfully sorry. There's a telephone in the Public House about a mile down the road. I suggest you use that.
Alex: But, missus, this is an emergency. It's a matter of life and death. My friend's lying in the middle of the road bleeding to death.

Catlady: Well, I'm very sorry, but I never open the door to strangers after dark.

Alex: Very well, madam. I suppose you can't be blamed for being suspicious with so many scoundrels and rogues of the night about. I'll try and get help at the pub then. I'm sorry if I disturbed you. Thank you very much. Good night.

Night. Exterior. Catlady House.

*The droogs put on their maskies and silently follow
Alex round to the rear of the house.*

Alex points to an open window on the first floor.

Alex: Dim, bend down. . . . I'm gonna get in that window and open the front door.

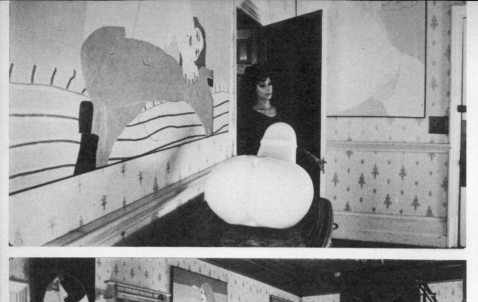

Night. Interior. Catlady House.

Catlady: Hullo, Radlett Police Station?
Police voice: Yes.
Catlady: Good evening. It's Miss Weathers at Woodmere Health Farm.
Police voice: Good evening, madam.
Catlady: Look, I'm frightfully sorry to bother you but something rather odd has just happened. Well, it's probably nothing at all, but you never know.
Police voice: You'd better tell me about it anyway.
Catlady: Well, a young man rang the bell asking to use the telephone. He said there had been some kind of accident. But the thing that caught my attention was what he said: the words he used sounded very much like what was quoted in the papers this morning, in connection with the writer and his wife who were assaulted last night.
Police voice: When did this all take place, madam?
Catlady: Just a few minutes ago...
Police voice: Well, I think we'd better send a patrol car round to have a look around.

Catlady Well, if you think that's necessary, but I'm quite sure he's gone away now.
Police voice: It'll be there in a few minutes.
Catlady: Oh . . . alright, fine. Thank you very much. Thank you.
Alex: Hi hi hi, there. At last we meet.

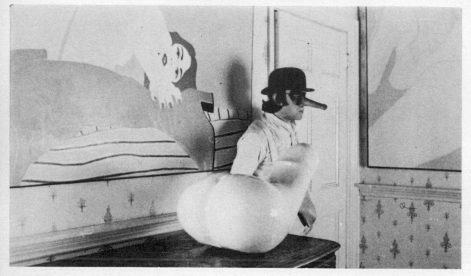

Our brief govoreet through the letter hole was not, shall we say, satisfactory, yes?

Catlady: Who are you?

How the hell did you get in here?
What the bloody hell do you think you're doing?

Alex: Naughty, naughty, naughty.

You filthy old soomka.

Catlady: Now listen here, you little bastard.
Just turn around and walk out of here the same
way as you came in.

Catlady: Leave that alone! Don't touch it.
It's a very important work of art.

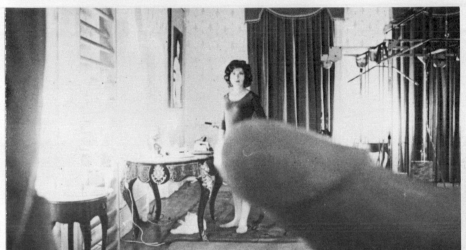

Well, what the bloody hell do you want?

Alex : Well, to be perfectly honest, madam, I'm taking part in an international students' contest

to see who can get the most points for selling magazines.

Catlady : Cut the shit, sonny, and get out of here before you get yourself into some very

serious trouble.

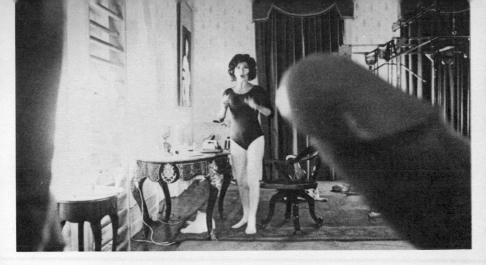

I told you to leave that alone.
Now get out of here before I throw you out.

Wretched, slummy bedbug. I'll teach you to break into real people's houses.

Catlady picks up bust of Beethoven and rushes at Alex.

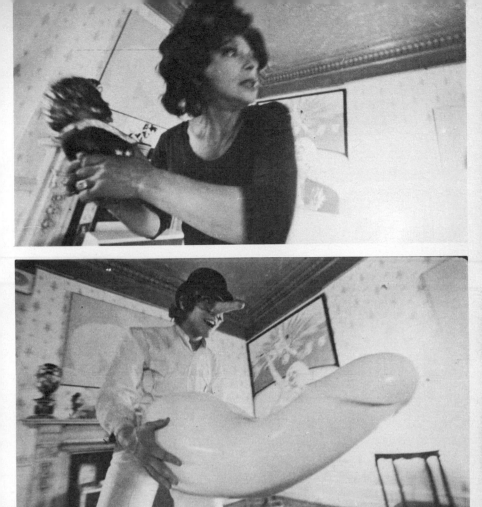

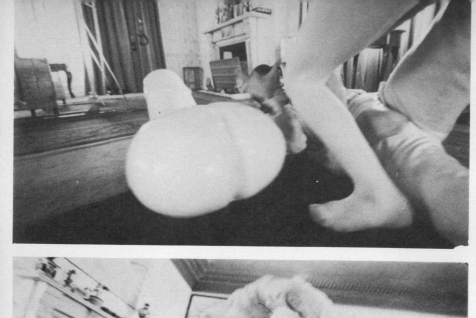
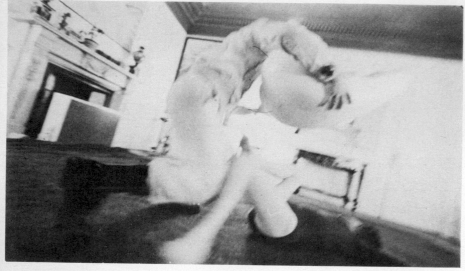
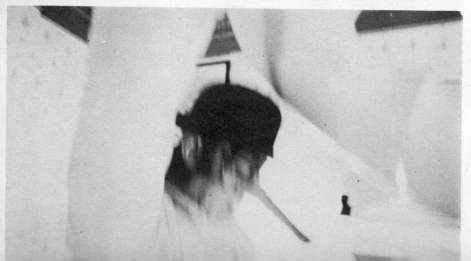

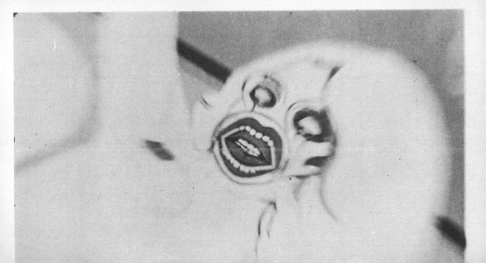

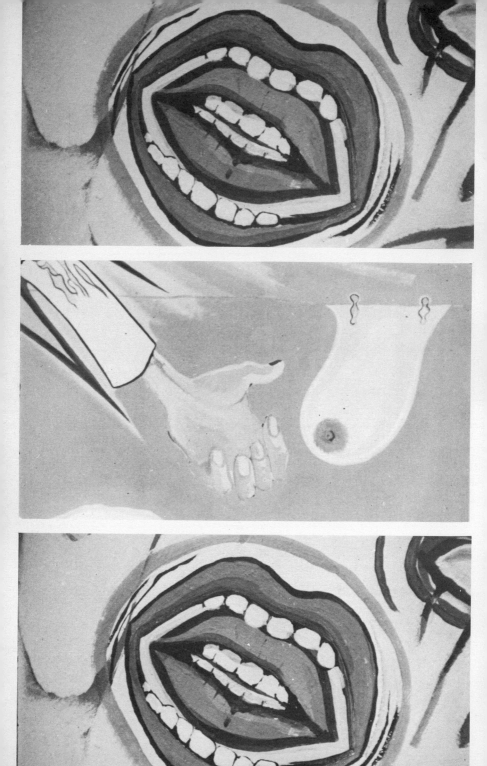

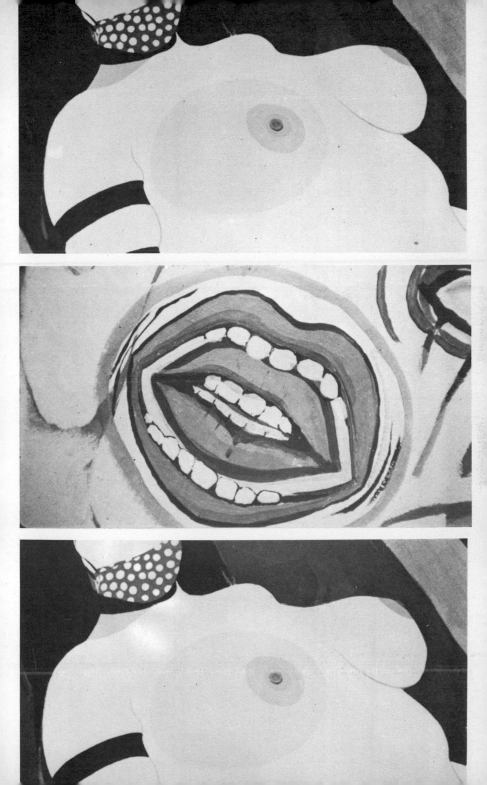

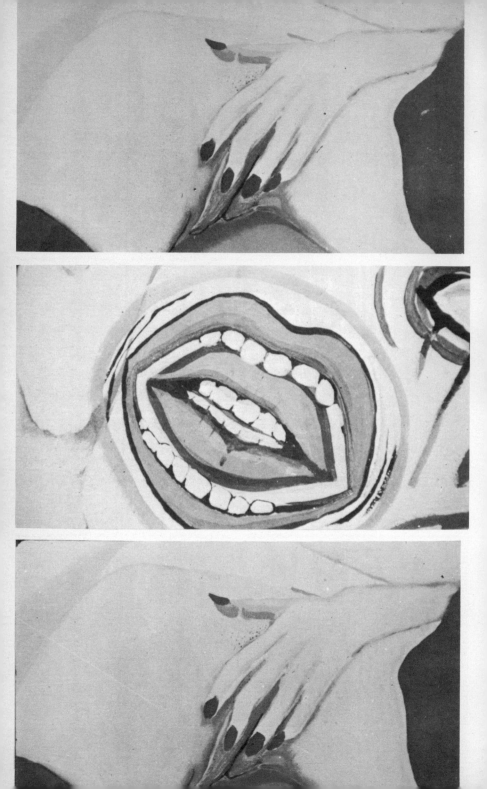

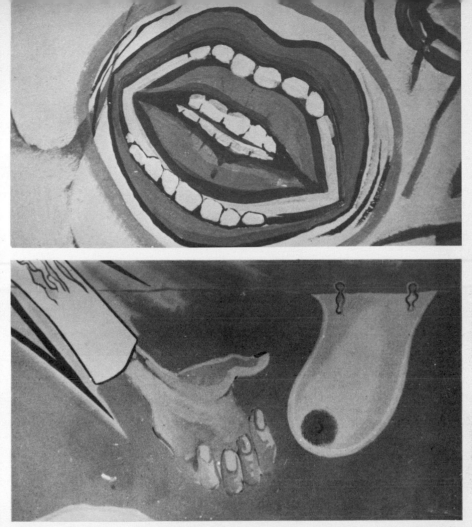
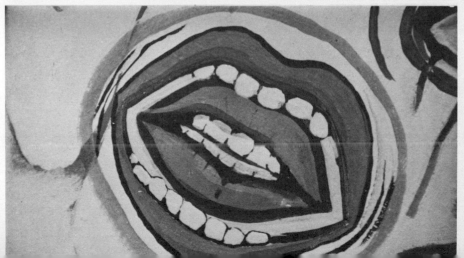

Sound of distant police siren.

Night. Exterior. Health Farm.

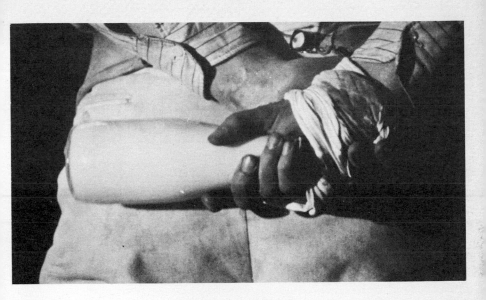

Alex exits.

Alex :   Come on. Let's go, the police are coming.
Dim :   One minoota, droogie.

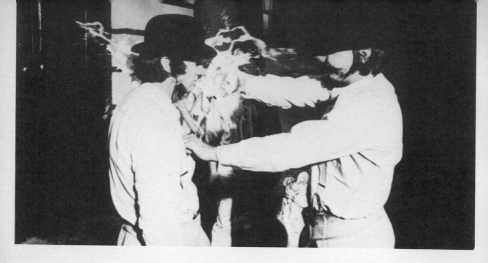

*Dim hits him with milk bottle. Alex falls to
the ground.*

Alex: I'm blind, you bastards! I'm blind!!!
I'm blind, you bastards!!! I can't see! O, you
bastards!!! I'm blind!

Reel 6

Night. Interior. Police HQ – Windowless, Interview room.

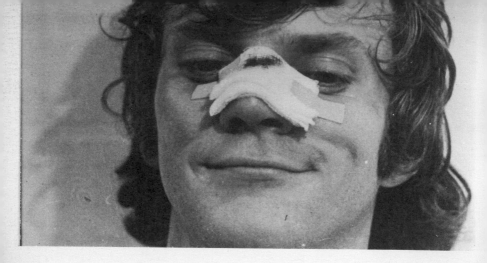

Alex: It's no good sitting there in hope, my little brothers. I won't say a single solitary slovo unless I have my lawyer here. I know the law, you bastards.

Inspector: Righty, right, Tom, we'll have to show our little friend Alex here that we know the law too, but that knowing the law isn't everything.

Tom: Nasty cut you've got there, little Alex. Shame . . . spoils all your beauty. Who gave you that then, eh? How did you do that then . . . eh . . . ?

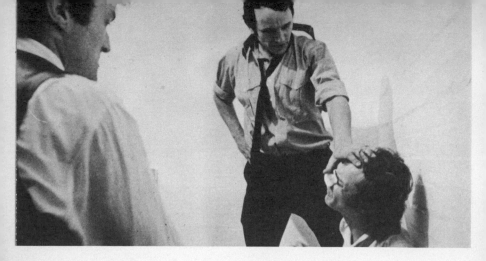

Alex burps in Tom's face. Tom brutally jams his thumb down on Alex's injured nose.

Alex: What was that for, you bastard?

Tom: That, is for your lady victim, you ghastly wretched scoundrel.

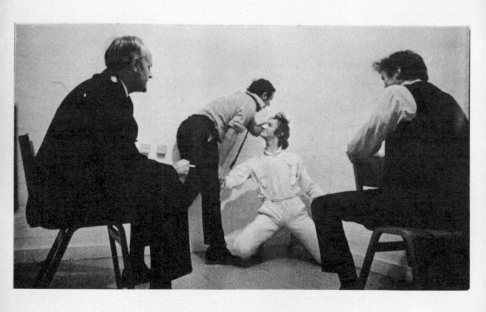

Alex grabs Tom's yarbles, He is beaten and kicked by the other detective.

Inspector: You rotten bastard!

Sergeant: Good evening, Mr. Deltoid.
Deltoid: Good evening, Sergeant.
Sergeant: They're in room 'B', sir.
Deltoid: Thank you very much.

Inspector exits interview room and bumps into Deltoid.

Inspector: Sergeant . . . ah, good evening, Mr. Deltoid.

Deltoid: Good evening, Inspector.

Sergeant: Would you like your tea now, sir?

Inspector: No, thank you, Sergeant, we'll have it later. May I have some paper towels, please?

Sergeant: Yes, sir.

Inspector: We're interrogating the prisoner now. Perhaps you'd care to come inside. Thank you very much.

Deltoid:
Evening, Sergeant. Evening all.

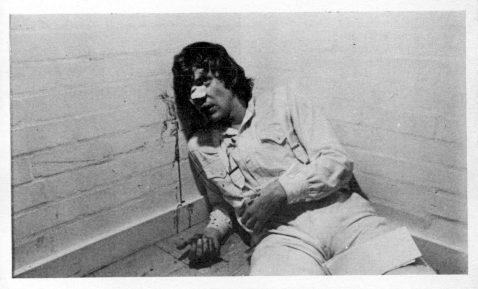

Dear, dear, this boy does look a mess doesn't he? Just look at the state of him.

Tom: Love's young nightmare, like.

Inspector: Violence makes violence. He resisted his lawful arrestors.

Deltoid: Well, this is the end of the line for me, the end of the line, yes ?

Alex: It wasn't me, brother, sir. Speak up for me, sir, for I'm not so bad. I was led on by the treachery of others, sir.

Inspector: Sings the roof off lovely, he does that.

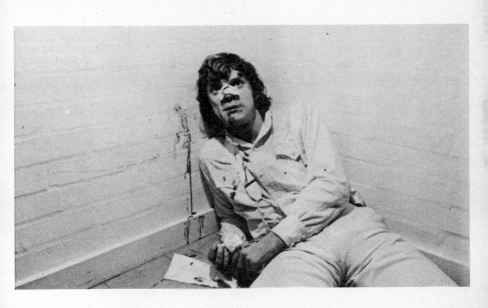

Alex: Where are my stinking traitorous droogs? Get them before they get away. It was all their idea, brothers. They forced me to do it. I'm innocent.

Deltoid :   You are now a murderer, little Alex.
A murderer.

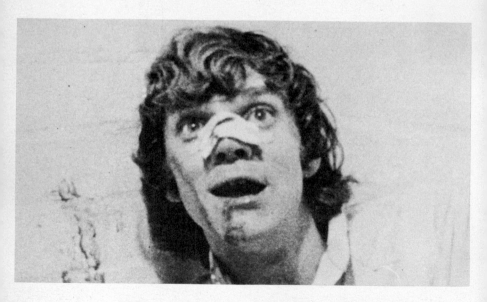

Alex :   It's not true, sir. It was only a slight
tolchock. She was breathing, I swear it.
Deltoid :   I've just come from the hospital.
Your victim has died.

Alex :   You try to frighten me, admit so,
sir. This is some new form of torture, say it,
brother, sir.

Deltoid: It will be your own torture. I hope to God it will torture you to madness.

Tom: If you'd care to give him a bash in the chops, sir, don't mind us. We'll hold him down. He must be a great disappointment to you, sir.

Deltoid spits in Alex's face.

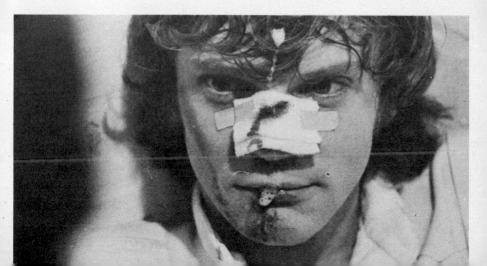

Day. Exterior. Aerial views of Prison.

Alex: *(Voice Over)* **This is the real weepy and like tragic part of the story beginning, O my brothers and only friends.**

After a trial with judges and a jury, and some very hard words

spoken against your friend and humble narrator, he was sentenced to 14 years

Day. Interior. Prison reception centre.

in Staja No. 84F, among smelly perverts and hardened prestoopnicks, the shock sending my dadda beating his bruised and krovvy rookers against unfair Bog in his Heaven, and my mum boohoohooing in her mother's grief, at her only child and son of her bosom like letting everybody down real horrowshow.

Guard: Morning. One up from Thames, Mister.
Warder: One up from Thames, sir.
Chief Guard: *[Who shouts everything.]* Right. Open up, Mister.
Warder: Yes, sir.

Guard: Good morning, sir. Here are the prisoner's committal forms.
Chief Guard: Thank you, Mister. Name?
Alex: Alexander de Large.

Chief Guard: You are now in H.M. Prison Parkmoor and from this moment you will address all prison officers as sir. Name?

Alex: Alexander de Large, sir.
Chief Guard: Sentence?
Alex: 14 years, sir.
Chief Guard: Crime?
Alex: Murder, sir.
Chief Guard: Right. Take the cuffs off him, Mister.
Chief Guard *(to Alex):* You are now 655321, and it is your duty to memorise that number.

Chief Guard *(to Guard)* :   Thank you,
Mister. Well done.
Guard: Thank you, Chief!

Chief Guard: Let the officer out!
Warder: Yes, sir.
Guard exits.

Chief Guard: Right, empty your pockets.

Alex moves to desk and leans on it.

Are you able to see the white line painted on
the floor directly behind you, 655321 ???

Alex: Yes, sir.
Chief Guard: Then your toes belong on the
other side of it!!!
Alex: Yes, sir.
Chief Guard: Right, carry on.
Alex tosses a bar of chocolate on the desk.
Chief Guard: Pick that up and put it down
properly.
Alex picks it up and puts it down again.

Chief Guard: One half bar of chocolate. One bunch of keys on white metal ring. One packet of cigarettes. Two plastic ball pens — one black, one red. One pocket comb — black plastic. One address book — imitation red leather. One ten penny piece. One white metal wristlet watch, "Timawrist", on a white metal expanding bracelet. Anything else in your pockets?

Alex: No, sir.

Chief Guard: Right, sign here, for your valuable property. The tobacco and chocolate you brought in, you lose that, as you are now convicted. Now over to the table and get undressed.

Alex walks to another table and begins to undress.

Now then, were you in police custody this morning?

Alex: No, sir.

Warder: One jacket — blue pinstripe.

Chief Guard: Prison custody?

Alex: Yes, sir. On remand, sir.

Warder: One necktie, blue.

Chief Guard: Religion?

Alex: C of E, sir.
Chief Guard: Do you mean the Church of England?
Alex: Yes, sir. The Church of England, sir.
Chief Guard: Brown hair, isn't it?
Alex: Fair hair, sir.
Chief Guard: Blue eyes?
Alex: Blue, sir.
Chief Guard: Do you wear eye glasses or contact lenses?
Alex: No, sir.
Warder: One shirt – blue, collar attached.
Chief Guard: Have you been receiving medical treatment for any serious illness?
Alex: No, sir.
Warder: One pair of boots – black leather, zippered. Worn.
Chief Guard: Have you ever had any mental illness?
Alex: No, sir.
Chief Guard: Do you wear any false teeth or any false limbs?
Alex: No, sir.
Warder: One pair of trousers – blue pinstripe.

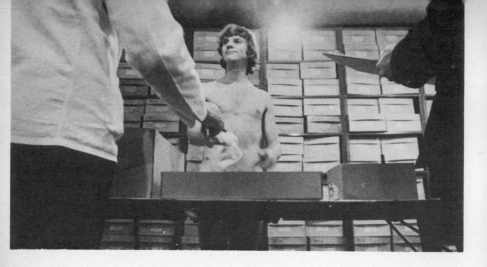

Chief Guard : Have you ever had any attacks of fainting or dizziness ?
Alex : No, sir.
Warder : One pair of socks – black.
Chief Guard : Are you an epileptic ?
Alex : No, sir.
Warder : One pair of underpants – white, with blue waistband.

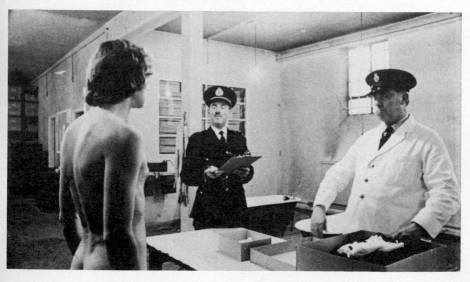

Chief Guard : Are you now, or have you ever been, a homosexual ?

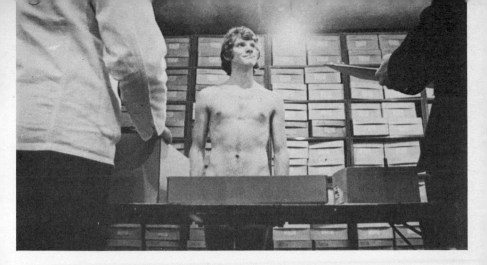

Alex: No, sir.

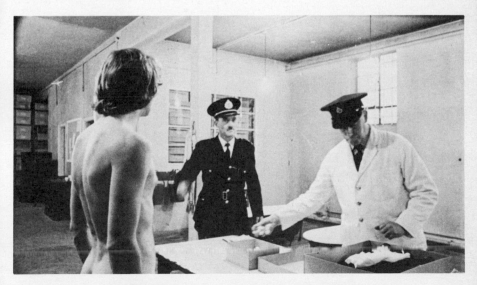

Chief Guard: Right, the mothballs, Mister.
Warder: Mothballs, sir.

Chief Guard: Now then, face the wall.
Bend over and touch your toes.

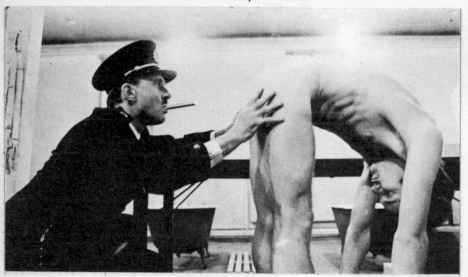

Any venereal disease?
Alex: No, sir.
Chief Guard: Crabs?
Alex: No, sir.
Chief Guard: Lice?
Alex: No, sir.
Chief Guard: Over there for a bath.
Alex: Yes, sir.
Warder: One for a bath.

Reel 7

Day. Interior. Prison Chapel.

Priest: What's it going to be then ? Is it
going to be in and out of institutions like this,
though more in than out for most of you ?
Or are you going to attend to the divine word
and realise the punishments that await
unrepentant sinners in the next world as well as this ?

A lot of idiots you are, selling your birthright for
a saucer of cold porridge, the thrill of theft, of

Prisoner blows kisses at Alex.

violence, the urge to live easy. Well, I ask you,

what is it worth ? When we have undeniable

proof, yes, incontrovertible evidence

that **Hell** exists. I know, I know, my friends.
I have **been** informed

in visions that there is a place darker
than any prison, hotter than any flame of human
fire, where souls of unrepentant criminal
sinners like yourselves. . .

A convict burps—all laugh.

Don't you laugh, damn you, don't you laugh!!
I say like yourselves, scream in endless and
unendurable agony.

Their skin rotting and peeling,
a fireball spinning in their screaming
guts. I know . . . oh yes, I know.

Someone blows raspberries.

Chief Guard: I saw you, 920537! I saw you!

There is an uproar.

Priest: Quiet. All right, you lot. We'll end by singing Hymn 258 in the Prisoners' Hymnal.

The singing begins.

Chief Guard: And, let's have a little reverence, you bastards.
Singing: *I was a wandering sheep.*

Chief Guard: Come on, sing up, damn you.
Singing: *I did not love . . .*
Chief Guard: Louder.
Singing: *. . . . the fold.*
I did not love my shepherd's voice.
I would not be controlled.

Chief Guard: Louder.
Singing: *I was a wayward child*
I did not love my home.
I did not love my Father's voice
I loved afar to roam.

Alex: *(Voice Over)* It had not been edifying, indeed not, being in this hellhole and human zoo for two years now, being kicked and tolchocked by brutal warders, and meeting leering criminals and perverts, ready to dribble all over a luscious young malchick like your storyteller.

Day. Interior. Prison Library—Alex reading the Bible.

Alex: *(Voice Over)* It was my rabbit to help the prison charlie with the Sunday service. He was a bolshy great burly bastard, but he was very fond of myself, me being very young, and also now very interested in the big book.

Alex: Move on there . . . Move along.
Move along there.
(Voice Over) I read all about the
scourging and the crowning with thorns
and I could viddy myself helping in and
even taking charge of the tolchocking and
the nailing in, being dressed in the height
of Roman fashion.

I didn't so much like the latter part of the book, which is more like all preachy talking than fighting and the old in-out.

I liked the parts where these old yahoodies
tolchock each other and then drink their
Hebrew vino,

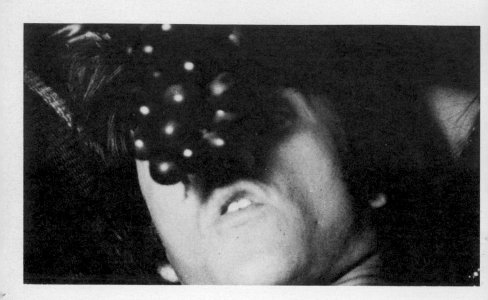

and getting onto the bed
with their wives' handmaidens.
That kept me going.

Priest: Seek not to be like evil men,

neither desire to be with them, because their minds studieth robberies and their lips speak deceits.

Alex: If thou lose hope being weary in the days of distress, thy strength shall be diminished.

Priest: Fine, my son, fine, fine.

Alex: Father, I have tried,have I not?

Priest: You have, my son.

Alex: I have done my best, have I not?

Priest: Indeed.

Alex: I've never been guilty of any institutional infraction, have I, Father?

Priest: You certainly have not, 655321. You've been very helpful and you've shown a genuine desire to reform.

Alex: Father, can I ask you a question in private?

Priest: Certainly, my son, certainly.

They walk in silence.

Is there something troubling you, my son? Don't be shy to speak up. Remember, I know of the urges that can trouble young men deprived of the society of women.

Alex: No, Father, it's nothing like that, Father. It's about this new thing they're all talking about, Father. About this new treatment that gets you out of prison in no time at all and makes sure you never get back in again.

Priest: Where did you hear about this? Whose been talking about these things?

Alex: These things get around, Father. Two warders talk as it might be, and somebody can't help overhearing what they say. Then somebody picks up a scrap of newspaper in the workshops and the newspaper tells all about it. How about putting me in for this new treatment, Father?

Priest: I take it you are referring to the Ludovico Technique?

Alex: I don't know what it's called, Father. All I know that it gets you out quickly and makes sure you never get back in again.

Priest: That is not proven 655321. In fact, it is only in the experimental stage at this moment.

Alex: It is being used, isn't it, Father?

Priest: It has not been used in this prison yet. The Governor has grave doubts about it, and I have heard that there are very serious dangers involved.

Alex: I don't care about the dangers, Father. I just want to be good. I want for the rest of my life to be one act of goodness.

Priest: The question is whether or not this technique really makes a man good. Goodness comes from within. Goodness is chosen. When a man cannot choose, he ceases to be a man.

Alex: I don't understand about the whys and wherefores, Father, I only know I want to be good.

Priest: Be patient, my son. Put your trust in the Lord.

Alex: Instruct thy son and he shall refresh thee and shall give delight to thy soul.

Priest: Amen.

Reel 8

Day. Exterior. Prison Exercise Yard.

Day. Interior. Prison Corridor. Enter the Minister, the Governor, the Chief Guard and other Guards.

Chief Guard: Mister!
Guard: All present and correct, sir!
Chief Guard: Right. All present and correct, sir.
Governor: Very good, chief.

Day. Interior. Alex's cell. Minister idly glances around and picks up a small bust of Beethoven.

Chief Guard: Prisoners, halt! Now pay attention! I want you in two lines! Up against that wall facing this way! Go on, move! Hurry up. Stop talking. Prisoners ready for inspection, sir.

Minister: How many to a cell?

Governor: Four in this block, sir.

Minister: Cram criminals together and what do you get – concentrated criminality, crime in the midst of punishment.

Governor: I agree, sir, what we need are larger prisons – more money.

Minister: Not a chance, my dear fellow. The Government can't be concerned any longer with outmoded penological theories. Soon we may be needing all our prison space for political offenders. Common criminals like these are best dealt with on a purely curative basis. Kill the criminal reflex, that's all. Full implementation in a year's time. Punishment means nothing to them, you can see that. They enjoy their so-called punishment.

Alex: You're absolutely right, sir.

Chief Guard: Shut your bleeding hole!

Minister: Who said that?

Alex: I did, sir.

Minister: What crime did you commit?

Alex: The accidental killing of a person, sir.

Chief Guard: He brutally murdered a woman, sir, in furtherance of theft. 14 years . . . sir!

Minister: Excellent. He's enterprising, aggressive, outgoing, young, bold, vicious. He'll do.

Governor: Well, fine . . .we could still look at C-Block.

Minister: No, no, no, that's enough. He's perfect. I want his records sent to me. This vicious young hoodlum will be transformed out of all recognition.

Alex: Thank you very much for this chance, sir.

Minister: Let's hope you make the most of it, my boy.

Governor: Shall we go to my office?

Minister: Thank you.

Governor: I don't suppose you know who that was this morning, do you? That was no less a personage than the Minister of the Interior. The new Minister of the Interior

Governor: Come in.

Chief Guard: Sir! 655321. Sir!

Governor: Very good, chief.

Chief Guard: Forward to the white line, toes behind it. Full name and number to the Governor.

Alex: Alexander de Large, sir. 655321, sir.

and what they call a very new broom. Well, these
new ridiculous ideas have come at last, and
orders are orders, though I may say to you, in
confidence, I do not approve. An eye for
an eye, I say. If someone hits you, you hit back,
do you not? Why then should not the State,
very severely hit by you brutal hooligans, not
hit back also? But the new view is to say no.

The new view is that we turn the bad into good. All of which seems to me to be grossly unjust. Eh?

Alex: Sir...

Chief Guard *(to Alex)* : Shut your filthy hole, you scum!

Governor: You are to be reformed.

Tomorrow you will go to this man, Brodsky. You will be leaving here. You will be transferred to the Ludovico Medical Facility. It is believed that you will be able to leave State Custody in a little over a fortnight.

I suppose that prospect pleases you ?
Chief Guard: Answer when the Governor
asks you a question.
Alex: Yes, sir. Thank you very much, sir. I've
done my best here, I really have, sir.

I'm very grateful to all concerned, sir.
Governor: Sign this, where it's marked.

Chief Guard: Don't read it, sign it!
Governor: It says that you are willing to have the residue of your sentence commuted to submission to the Ludovico treatment... and this

... and another copy.

Alex: *(Voice Over)* **The next morning, I was taken to the Ludovico Medical Facility outside the town centre, and I felt a malenky bit sad having to say goodbye to the old Staja, as you always will when you leave a place you've like gotten used to.**

Day. Exterior/Interior. Ludovico Medical Facility

Chief Guard: Right, halt the prisoner. Good morning, sir. I'm Chief Officer Barnes. I've got 655321 on a transfer from Parkmoor to the Ludovico Centre, sir.

Doctor: Good morning. Yes, we've been expecting you. I'm Doctor Alcott.

Chief Guard: Doctor Alcott.

Chief Guard checks the name.

Very good, sir.

Are you prepared to accept the prisoner, sir?

Doctor: Yes, of course.

Chief Guard: Well, I wonder if you'd mind signing these transfer documents, sir?

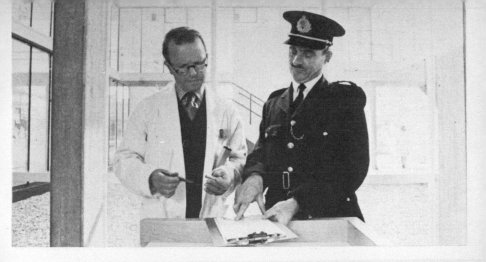

There, sir. . . and there, sir . . . and there.
Thank you, sir.

Prisoner and escort move forward!

Halt!
Excuse me, sir. Is that the officer that is to take
charge of the prisoner. sir ?

The officer moves forward and takes Alex's arm.

If I may offer a word of advice, Doc. You'll have to watch this one. A right brutal bastard he has been and will be again, in spite of all his sucking up to the prison Chaplain, and reading the Bible.

Doctor: Oh, I think we can manage things. Charlie, will you show the young man to his room now?

Charlie: Right, sir. Come this way, please.

They exit.

Reel 9

Day. Hall outside Alex's room – Ludovico Centre.
Enter Dr. Branom and Nurse.

Dr. Branom *(to the guard outside door)*
Good morning, Charlie.
Charlie: Good morning, Doctor.

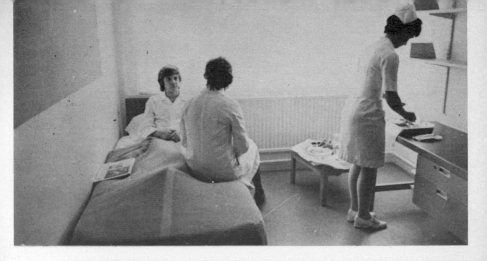

Dr. Branom: Good morning, Alex. My name is Doctor Branom. I'm Dr. Brodsky's assistant.
Alex: Good morning, missus. Lovely day, isn't it?
Dr. Branom: Yes, indeed it is. May I take this? And how're you feeling this morning?
Alex: Fine, fine.

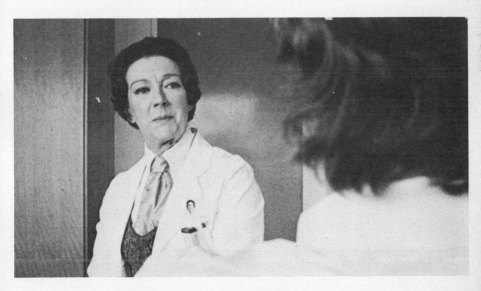

Dr. Branom: Good. Now in a few minutes you'll meet Dr. Brodsky and we'll begin your treatment.

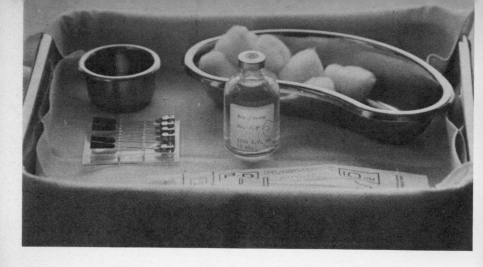

You're a very lucky boy to have been chosen.

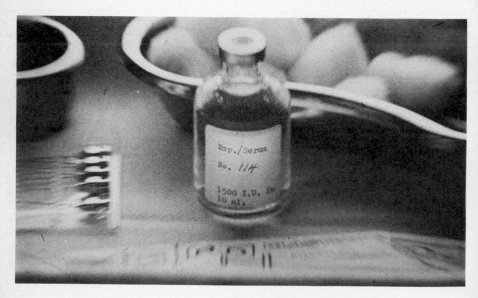

Alex: I realise that, missus, and I'm very
grateful to all concerned.

Dr. Branom: We're going to be friends then, aren't we, Alex?

Nurse fills hypo.

Alex: I hope so, missus.

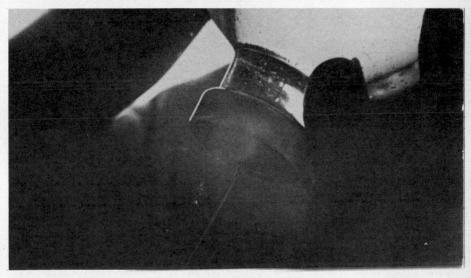

What's the hypo for then?
Gonna send me to sleep?
Dr. Branom: Oh no, nothing of the sort.

Alex: Vitamins, will it be then?
Dr. Branom: Something like that.

You're a little undernourished, so after each meal
we're going to give you a shot. Roll over
on your right side, please, loosen your pyjama
pants and pull them half way down.

Dr. Branom gives him the shot.
Alex: What exactly is the treatment here going to be then ?

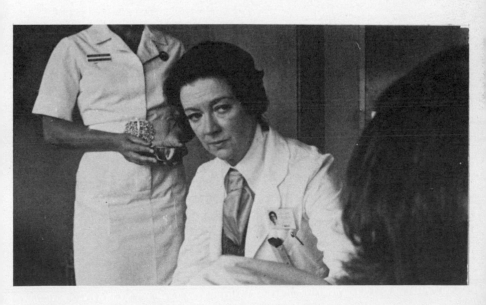

Dr. Branom: Oh, it's quite simple really.
We're just going to show you some films.
Alex: You mean like going to the pictures ?
Dr. Branom: Something like that.

Alex: Well, that's good. I like to viddy the old films now and again.

Day. Interior. Audio Visual Theater.

Alex: *(Voice Over)* And viddy films, I would. Where I was taken to, brothers, was like no sinny I ever viddied before.

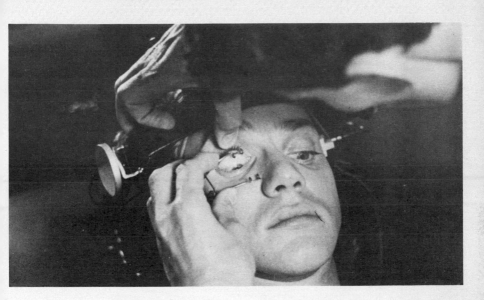

I was bound up in a straitjacket and my gulliver was strapped to a headrest with like wires running away from it. Then they clamped like lidlocks on my eyes so that I could not shut them no matter how hard I tried. It seemed a bit crazy to me, but I let them get on with what they wanted to get on with. If I was to be a free young malchick again in a fortnight's time, I would put up with much in the meantime, O my brothers.

So far, the first film was a very good, professional piece of sinny, like it was done in Hollywood.

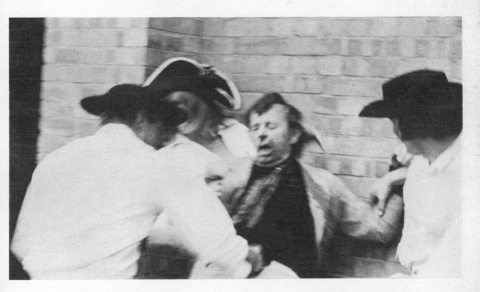

The sounds were real horrowshow. You could slooshy the screams and moans very realistic, and you could even get the heavy breathing and panting of the

tolchocking malchicks at the same time.
And then, what do you know, soon our
dear old friend,

the red, red vino on tap, the same in all places
like it's put out by the same big firm,
began to flow.

It was beautiful. It's funny how the colours of the real world only seem really real when you viddy them on the screen.

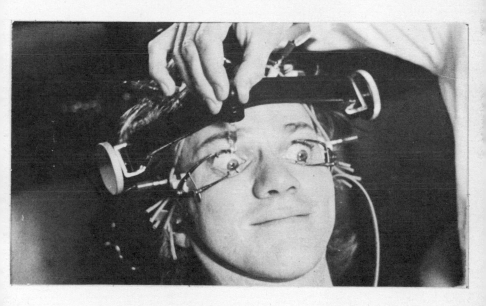

Now all the time I was watching this, I was beginning to get very aware of like not feeling all that well, and this I put down to all the rich food and vitamins, but I tried to forget this, concentrating on the next film,

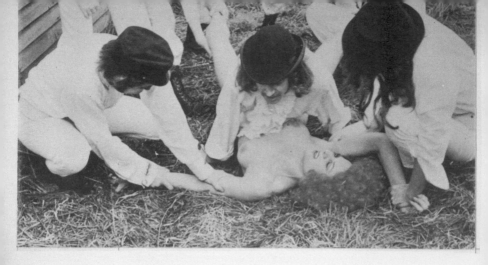

which jumped right away on a young
devotchka

who was being given the old in-out, in-out
first by one malchick,

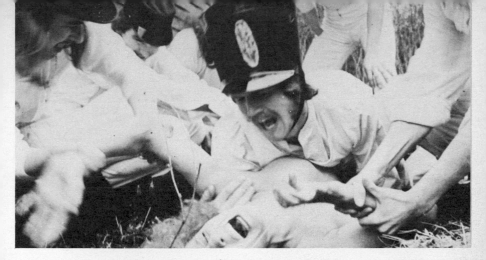

then another,

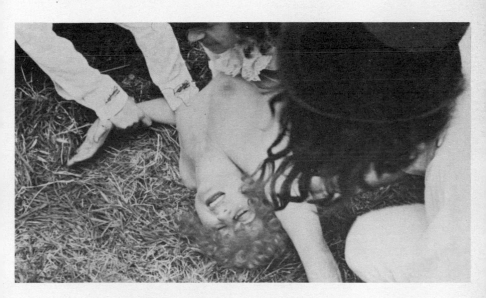

then another.

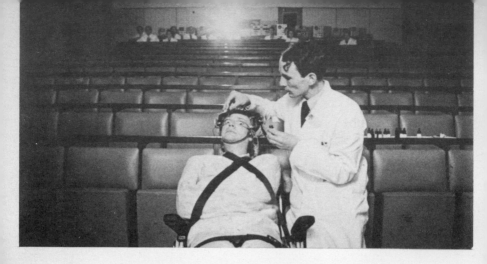

When it came to the sixth or seventh
malchick, leering and smecking and then
going into it, I began to feel really sick.

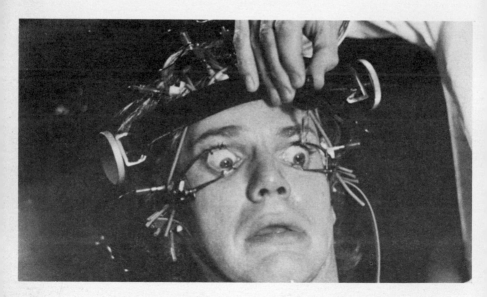

But I could not shut my glazzies. And even
if I tried to move my glazz-balls about, I
still could not get out of the line of fire of
this picture.

Alex: Get me up! I want to be sick! Get
something for me to be sick in! I want to be sick!

Dr. Brodsky: *(softly to those around him)*
Very soon now, the drug will cause the subject
to experience a death-like paralysis, together
with deep feelings of terror and helplessness.
Alex: *(o.s.)* I can't stand it any more.
Dr. Brodsky: One of our early test subjects
described it as being like death, a sense of
stifling or drowning,

and it is during this period we have found
that the subject will make his most

rewarding associations between his catastrophic
experience-environment and the violence he sees.

Alex: *(screams o.s.)* Leave me glazzies! Leave me
glazzies!

Day. Interior. Alex's room. Ludovico Centre.

Dr. Branom: Dr. Brodsky is pleased with
you. You've made a very positive response.

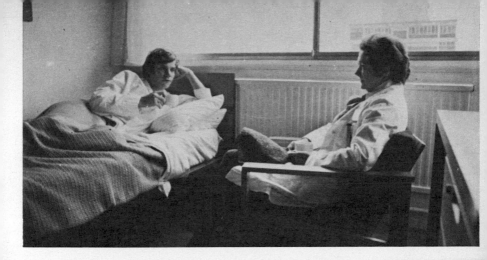

Now tomorrow there will be two sessions, of
course, morning and afternoon.

Alex: You mean I have to viddy two sessions
in one day?

Dr. Branom: I imagine you'll be feeling a
little bit limp by the end of the day, but we
have to be hard on you.

You have to be cured.

Alex: It was horrible.

Dr. Branom: Of course it was horrible. Violence is a very horrible thing. That's what you're learning now. Your body is learning it.

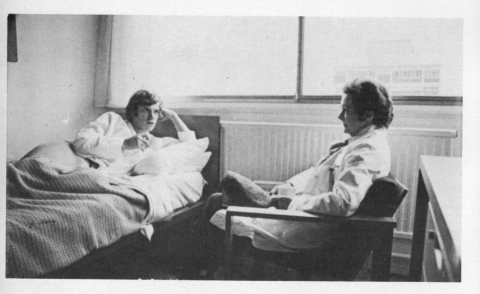

Alex: I just don't understand about feeling sick the way I did. I never used to feel sick before. I used to feel like the very opposite. I mean, doing it or watching it, I used to feel real horrorshow.

Dr. Branom: You felt ill this afternoon because you're getting better. You see, when we are healthy, we respond to the presence of the hateful with fear and nausea. You're becoming healthy, that's all. By this time tomorrow, you'll be healthier still.

Interior. Audio-Visual Theater.
Newsreels and Beethoven's Ninth Symphony.

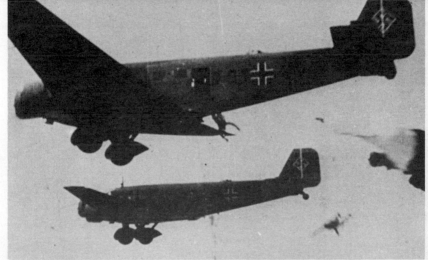

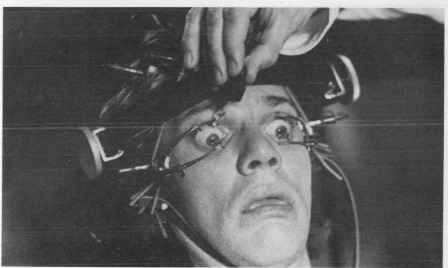

Alex: *(Voice Over)* It was the next day, brothers, and I had truly done my best, morning and afternoon, to play it their way and sit, like a horrorshow co-operative malchick, in the chair of torture, while they flashed nasty bits of ultra-violence on the screen. Though not on the soundtrack, my brothers. The only sound being music. Then I noticed in all my pain and sickness what music it was that like cracked and boomed –

it was Ludwig van – Ninth Symphony, fourth movement.

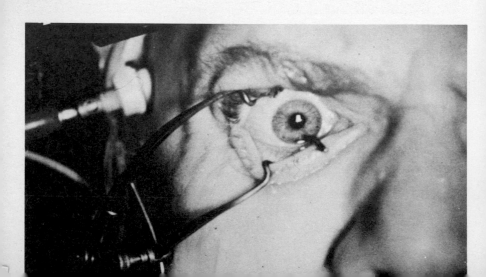

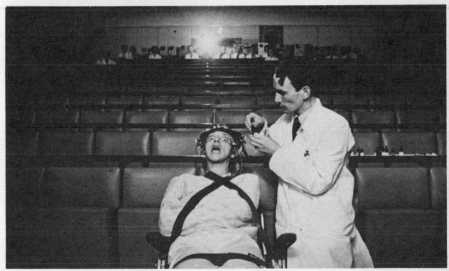

Alex: Stop it!!! Stop it!!! Please!!! I beg you!!! It's a *sin* . . .

It's a *sin* . . . It's a *sin*!

Dr. Brodsky: Sin? What's all this about sin?

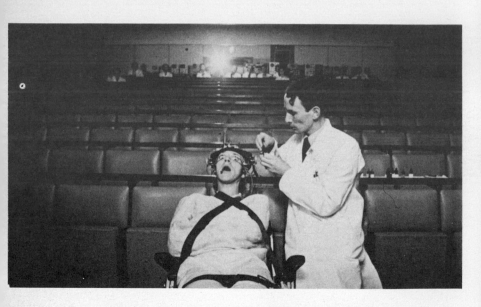

Alex: That !!! Using Ludwig van like that!
He did no harm to anyone. Beethoven just
wrote music!

Dr. Branom: Are you referring to the background score?

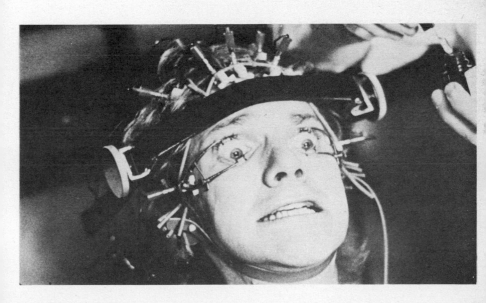

Alex: Yes.!!

Dr. Branom: You've heard Beethoven
before?

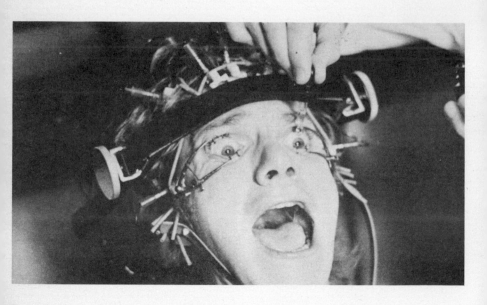

Alex: Yes.!!!

Dr. Brodsky: So you're keen on music?

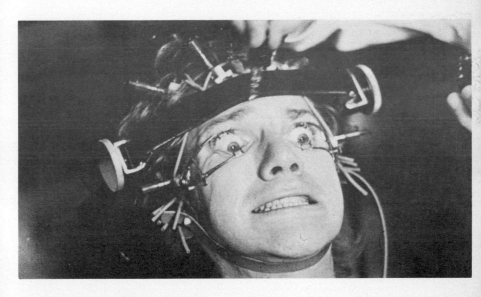

Alex: Yes.!!

Dr. Brodsky: *(To Branom)* It can't be helped.
Here's the punishment element perhaps. The
Governor ought to be pleased . . . I'm sorry, Alex, this
is for your own good. You'll have to bear with us
for a while.

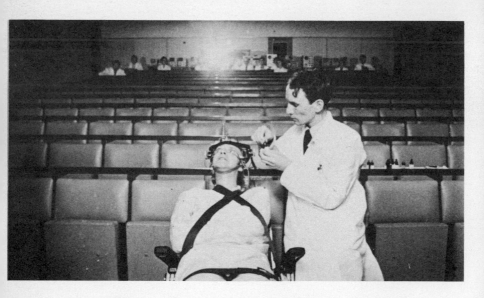

Alex: But it's not fair! It's not fair I should
feel ill when I hear lovely, lovely Ludwig van!

Dr. Brodsky: You must take your chance, boy.

The choice has been all yours.

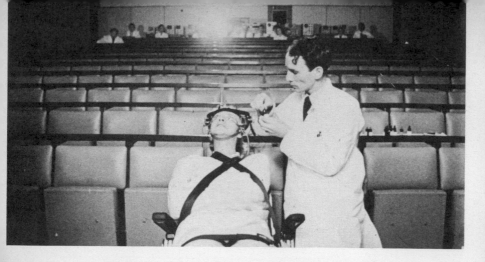

Alex: You needn't take it any further, sir. You've proved to me that all this ultra-violence and killing is wrong, wrong and terribly wrong.

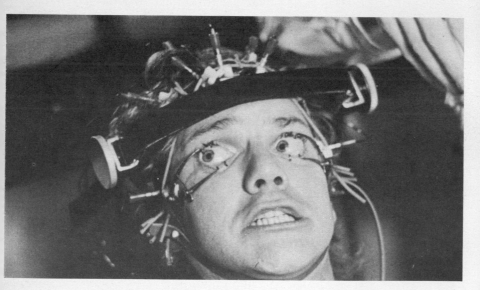

I've learned my lesson, sir. I see now what I've never seen before. I'm cured, praise God!!

Dr. Brodsky: You're not cured yet, boy.

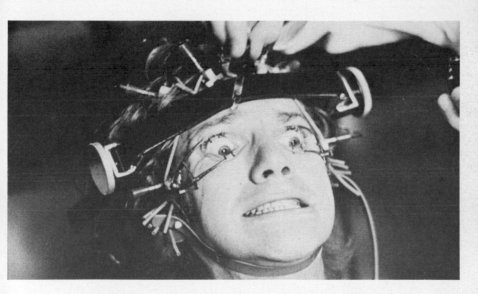

Alex: But sir, missus, I see that it's wrong! It's wrong because it's like against society. It's wrong because everybody has the right to live and be happy without being tolchocked and knifed.

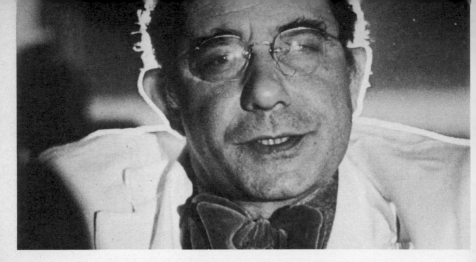

Dr. Brodsky: No, no, boy. You really must leave it to us, but be cheerful about it. In less than a fortnight now, you will be a free man.

Reel 10

Day. Interior. Auditorium — VIP Audience. Alex enters. Minister rises to speak.

Minister: Ladies and Gentlemen, at this stage, we introduce the subject himself. He is, as you will perceive, fit and well nourished. He comes straight from a night's sleep and a good breakfast, undrugged, unhypnotised.

Tomorrow, we send him out with confidence into the world again, as decent a lad as you would meet on a May morning.

What a change is here, Ladies and Gentlemen,
from the wretched hoodlum the State committed to
unprofitable punishment some two years ago.
Unchanged after two years.

Unchanged, do I say? — not quite.
Prison taught him the false smile,
the rubbed hand of hypocrisy,

the fawning, greased obsequious leer. Other
vices it taught him, as well as confirming him in
those he had long practiced before.

Our party promised to restore law and order and
to make the streets safe again for the ordinary peace-
loving citizen. This pledge is now about to
become a reality. Ladies and Gentlemen, today
is an historic moment. The problem of criminal
violence is soon to be a thing of the past. But
enough of words. Actions speak louder than.
Action now. Observe all.

Polite applause. Minister sits.

Junior Minister: Our necks are out a long way on this, Minister.

Minister: I have complete faith in Brodsky. If the polls are right, we have nothing to lose.

Lardface enters.

Lardface: Hello, heap of dirt. Pooh, you don't wash much do you, judging by the horrible smell?

Alex: Why do you say that, brother? I had a shower this morning.
Lardface: Oh, he had a shower this morning. You trying to call me a liar?
Alex: No, brother.

Lardface: Then you must think I'm awfully stupid.

Lardface slaps Alex's face.

Alex: Why did you do that brother? I've never done wrong to you.

Lardface: You want to know why I did that? Well, you see,

I do this
Stamps on toe
. . . and that
Twists his nose
. . . and this
Pulls his ear

Pushes him over

because I don't like your horrible type, do I?
And if you want to start something . . . if you
want to start . . . well, you just go ahead! Go
on . . . please do.

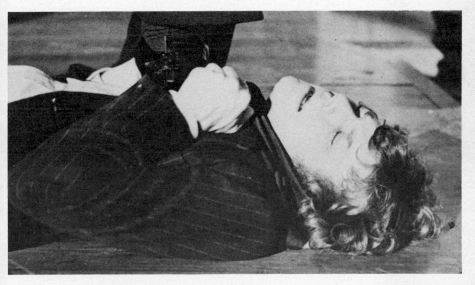

Go on.
Alex: I'm gonna be sick! I'm gonna be sick!
Lardface: You're gonna be sick are you?
Alex: I'm gonna be sick. Please let me get up.

Lardface: You want to get up?
Now you listen to me. If you want to get up,
you gotta do something for me. Here. Here. You
see that? You see that shoe?

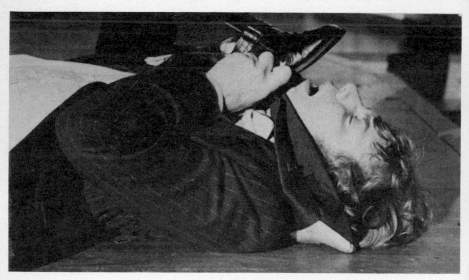

Well, I want you to lick it. Go on.

Lick it!

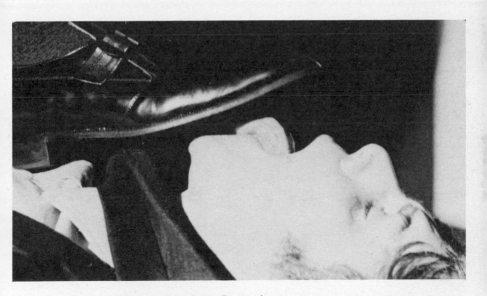

Alex: *(Voice Over)* And, O my brothers, would you believe your faithful friend and long suffering narrator pushed out his red yahzik a mile-and-a-half to lick the grahzny, vonny boots.

Lardface: That's it! And again.

Alex: *(Voice Over)* The horrible killing sickness had whooshed up, and turned the like joy of battle

into a feeling I was going to snuff it.
Lardface: And again. Nice and clean
Minister: Thank you very much.

That will do very well.
Lardface: Thank you very much, Ladies and
Gentlemen. Thank you very much. Thank you.

Bows and polite applause. Lardface exits.

Girl enters.

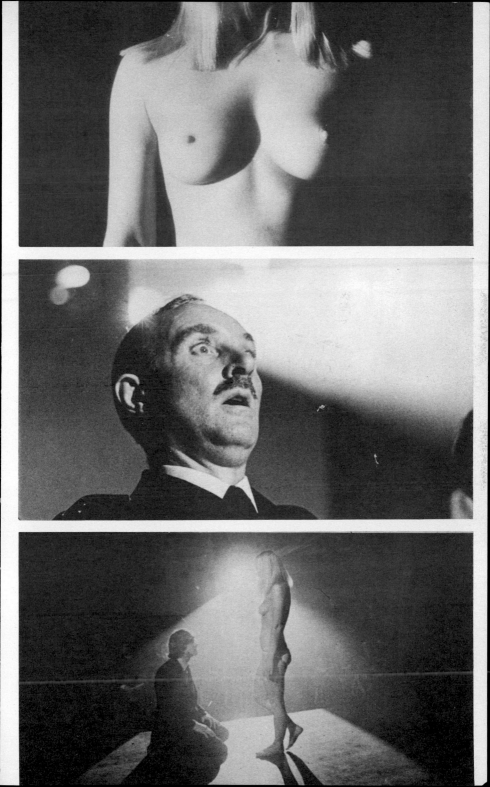

Alex: *(Voice Over)* She came towards me with the light like it was the like

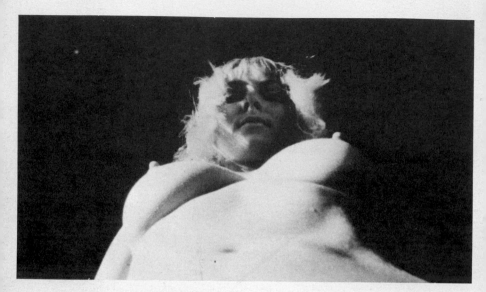

light of heavenly grace, and the first thing that flashed into my gulliver was that I'd like to have her right down there on the floor

with the old in-out, real savage.

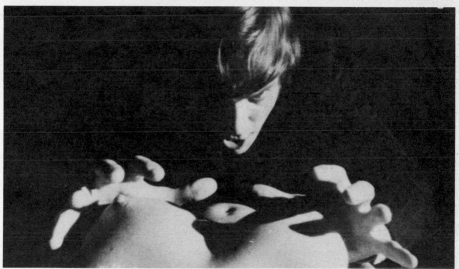

But as quick as a shot came the sickness, like a detective that had been watching around the corner

Retching, Alex sinks to the floor.

and now followed to make his arrest.

Minister: Enough,

thank you very much.
Thank you, my dear.

Not feeling too bad now, are you?
(burping and breathing heavily)

Alex: No, sir. Feel really great, sir.
Minister: Good.
Alex: Was it alright, sir? Did I do well, sir?
Minister: Fine, my boy, absolutely fine.
You see, Ladies and Gentlemen,

our subject is impelled towards the good by
paradoxically being impelled towards evil.
The intention to act violently is accompanied
by strong feelings of physical distress.
To counter these, the subject has to switch

to a diametrically opposed attitude. Any questions?

Priest: Choice!

The boy has no real choice, has he?
Self interest, the fear of physical pain drove
him to that grotesque act of self abasement.

Its insincerity was clearly to be seen.
He ceases to be a wrongdoer. He ceases
also to be a creature capable of moral choice.
Minister: Padre, these are subtleties! We
are not concerned with motives, with the
higher ethics. We are concerned only with
cutting down crime.

And with relieving the ghastly
congestion in our prisons.

He will be your true Christian, ready to turn the other cheek, ready to be crucified rather than crucify. Sick to the very heart at the thought even of killing a fly. Reclamation, joy before the angels of God. The point is that it works!

Alex: *(Voice Over)* **And the very next day, your Friend and Humble Narrator was a free man.**

Reel 11

Day. Interior. Alex's Flat. Alex enters. A radio is playing off screen.

Pee: Son!

Alex: Hi, hi, hi there, my Pee and Em.

All three look up startled.

Em: Alex!

Alex: Mum. How are you, love? Nice to see

Dad!

Pee: Hullo, lad. What a surprise, good to see you!

Alex: Keeping fit?

Pee: Oh, aye.

Alex: How are you then, how are you?

Pee: Oh, fine, fine. Keeping out of trouble, you know.

Alex: Well, I'm back!

Pee: Aye . . . Good to see you back.
Em: Why didn't you let us know what was happening, son?
Alex: Sorry, Em.

I wanted it to be like a big surprise for you and Pee.

Pee: It's a surprise all right . . . a bit bewildering too.

Em: We've only just read about it in morning papers.

Pee: Aye, you should have let us know, lad.

Not that we're not very pleased to see you
again, and all cured too, eh?

Alex: That's right, dad. They did a great job
on me.

I'm completely reformed.
Well, still the same old place, then, eh?

Pee: Oh, aye, aye.

Alex: *(stage whisper)* Hey, Dad, there's a strange-looking fella sitting in the sofa

munchy wunching lomticks of toast.

Pee: That's Joe. He . . . he lives here now. The lodger. That's what he is. He rents your room.

Alex : How do you do, Joe ? Find the room comfortable do you ? No complaints ?
Joe : I've heard about you. I know what you've done.

Breaking the hearts of your poor grieving parents. So you're back, eh ? You're back to make life a misery for your lovely parents once more, is that it ? Well, over my dead corpse you will because, you see, they've let me be more like a son to them than like a lodger.

Alex cocks his arm for a punch which causes him to retch violently.

Em: Joe!!! Joe!!! Don't go fighting in here, boys.

Alex burping and retching.

Joe: Well, do put your hand over your mouth, please, it's bloody revolting.

Alex stumbles to a chair and sits.

Pee: Are you all right, lad?

Em: Dad . . . it's the treatment.

Joe: Well, it's disgusting. I mean, it's enough to put you off your food.

Em: Oh, leave him be, Joe, it's the treatment.

Pee: Do you think we ought to do something?

Em: Would you like me to make you a nice cup of tea, son?

Alex nods.

Alex: What have you done with all my own personal things?

Pee: Oh, well, that was all took away, son, by the Police. New regulations, see, about compensation for the victims.

Alex: What about Basil? Where's my snake?

Pee: Well, he met with like an accident.
He . . . he passed away.

Tears come to Alex's eyes.

Alex: What's gonna happen to me then? I mean that's my room he's in,

there's no denying that.
This is my home, also. What suggestions have you, my Pee and Em, to make?

Pee: Well, all this needs thinking about, son.
I mean, we can't very well just kick Joe out.
Not just like that, can we? I mean, Joe's
here doing a job, a contract it is, two years . . .
and we made like an arrangement, didn't we
Joe? You see, son,

Joe's paid next month's
rent already so . . . well, whatever we may do in
the future, we can't just say to Joe to get out,
now, can we?
Joe: No, but there's much more than that,
though.

I mean I've got you two to think of.
You've been like a father and mother to me.
Well, it wouldn't be fair now or right, I mean,
for me to go off and leave you two to the
tender mercies of this young monster, who's
been like no real son at all.

Look, he's weeping now. But
that's all his craft and artfulness.

Let him go and find a room somewhere else.
Let him learn the errors of his way, and that a
bad boy like he's been doesn't deserve such a
good mum and dad as he's had.

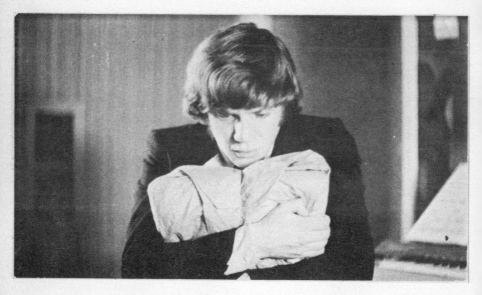

Alex: Alright. I know how things are now.

I've suffered and I've suffered and I've suffered,
and everybody wants me to go on suffering.

Joe: You've made others suffer. It's only
right that you should suffer proper. You know

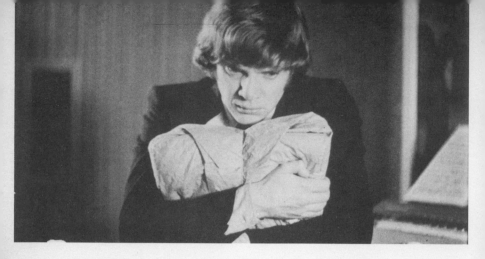

I've been told everything you've done, sitting
here at night round the family table, and pretty
shocking it was to listen to.

It made me real sick, a lot of it did.
Now look what you've gone
and done to your mother.
Em boo-hooing.
All right . . . come on, it's all right . . .

Alex rises.

Alex: Right, I'm leaving now. You won't ever viddy me no more. I'll make me own way. Thank you very much. Let it lie heavy on your consciences.

Pee: Now, don't take it like that, son.

Alex exits amidst loud boo-hooing from Em.

Reel 12

Day. Exterior. Thames Embankment.

Tramp: Can you spare some cutter, me
brother? Can you spare some cutter, me
brother?

Can you spare some cutter, me brother? . . .

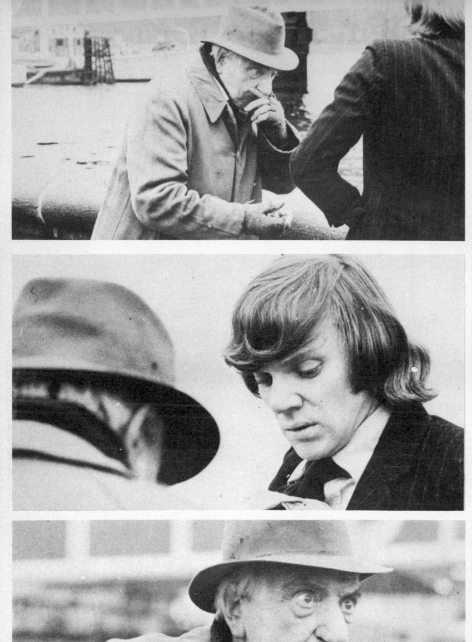

Thanks, brother.

Jamey Mack! Be the hokey fly!

Holy Mother of God and all the blessed saints
in heaven preserve us!!

I never forget a face, by God!!
I never forget *any* face!
Alex:　Leave me alone, brother. I've never
seen you before.

Tramp: This is the poisonous young swine that near done me in. Him and his friends, they beat me and kicked me and punched me. Stop him . . . stop him. They laughed at my blood and my moans. This murderous young pig.

Alex: *(Voice Over)* Then there was like a sea of dirty smelly old men, trying to get at your Humble Narrator, with their feeble rookers and horny old claws.

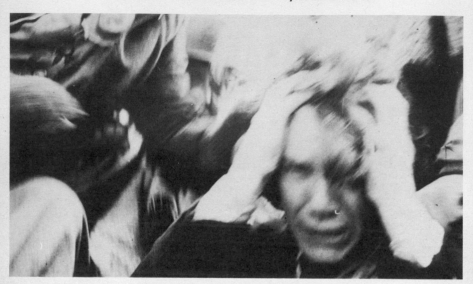

It was old age having a go at youth,

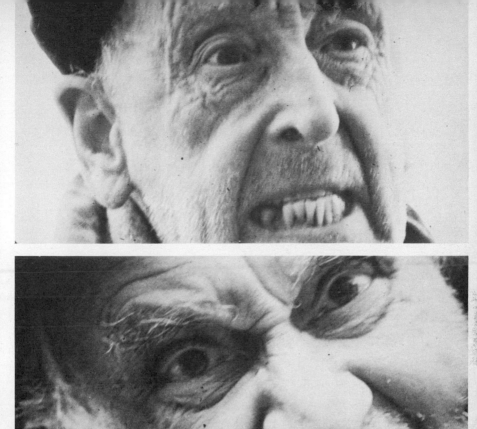
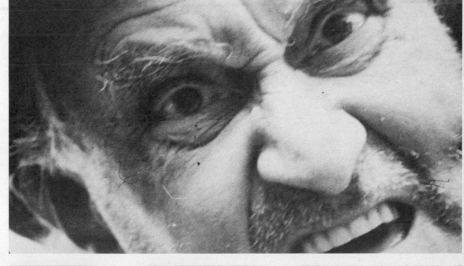
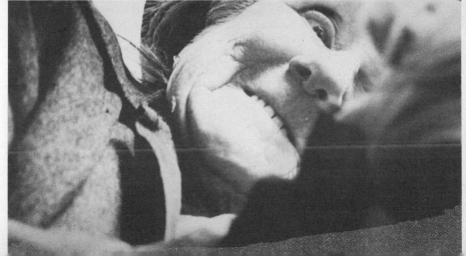

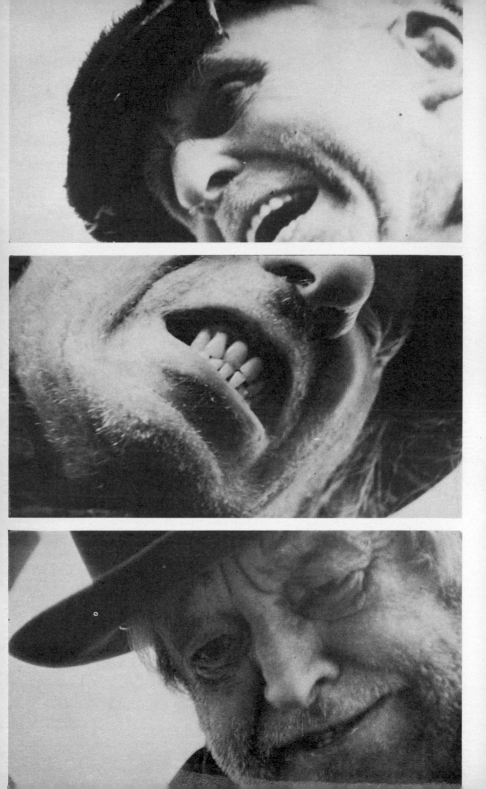

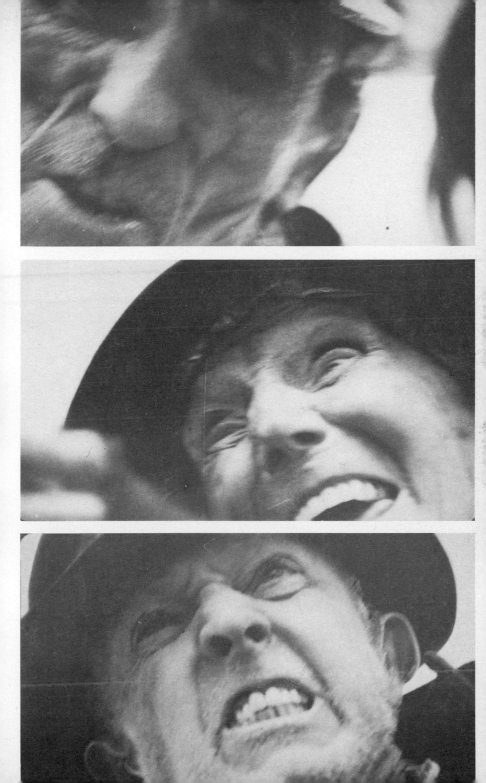

and I daren't do a single solitary thing,
O my brothers,
it being better to be hit at like that than
want to sick and feel that horrible pain.

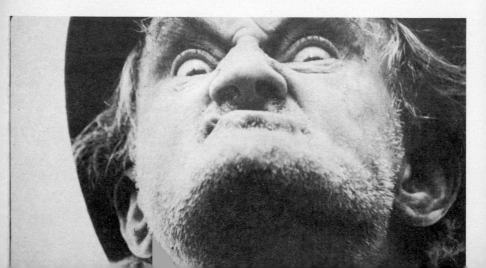

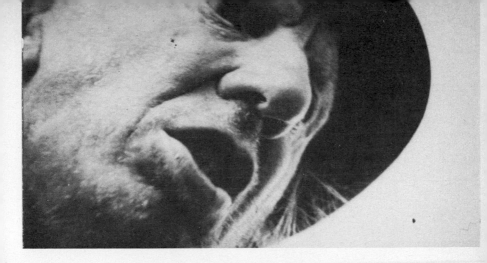

Tramps: Young hooligan . . . Vagabond . . .
Kill him . . . Villain . . .

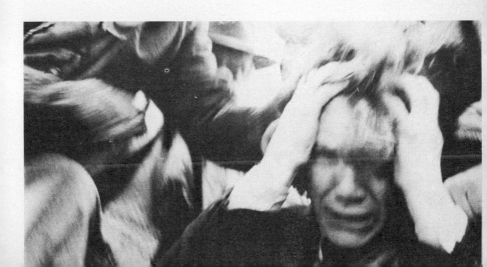

Enter two policemen.

1st Policeman: All right, all right, stop it now. Come on, stop breaking the State's peace, you naughty boys. Back away . . . Come on! Away with you. What's the trouble, sir?

Alex recognizes Dim and Georgie, now policemen.

Alex: Oh, no!

Dim: Well. Well, well, well, well, well, well, well. If it isn't little Alex?

Long time no viddy, droog. How goes?
Alex: It's impossible. I don't believe it.

Georgie: Evidence of the old glazzies.
Nothing up our sleeves. No magic, little Alex.
A job for two who are now of job age.

The Police.

Day. Exterior. Country Road.

Police car pulls to a stop. Dim and Georgie lead handcuffed Alex out.

Dim: Come on, Alex. Come for walkies.

Alex: Come, come, come, my little droogies, I just don't get this at all. The old days are dead and gone. For what I did in the past I've been punished.

Dim: Punished, yes.

Alex: I've been cured.

Dim: Cured, yes. That was read out to us. The Inspector read it all out to us. He said it was a very good way.

Alex: But what is all this? It was them that went for me brothers. You're not on their side and can't be. You can't be, Dim. It was someone we fillied with back in the old days, trying to get his own little bit of revenge, after all this time. Remember, Dim?

Dim: Long time is right. I don't remember them days too horrorshow. Don't call me Dim no more, either. Officer, call me.

Georgie: Enough is remembered, though, little Alex.

Dim: This is to make sure you stay cured.

Georgie hits Alex in the stomach with his blackjack, doubling him over. Dim pushes his head under the water and holds it there, while Georgie methodically beats him with his blackjack.

Georgie: That's enough, droogie . . .
Dim: A bit more, he's still kicking.
They pull Alex out, gasping for breath.

Cured, are you ? Are you cured ?
Be viddying you some more, some time, droogie.

Night. Exterior. "Home" Rain. Alex stumbling down the road.

Alex: *(Voice Over)* **Where was I to go, who had no home and no money? I cried for myself. Home, home, home. It was home I was wanting**

Night. Exterior "Home". Rain.

**and it was Home I came to, brothers,
not realising in the state I was in,
where I was and had been before.**

Reel 13

Interior. "Home".
Door chime rings.

Mr. Alexander: Who on earth could that be ?

Julian: I'll see who it is.

He goes to the door.

Yes, what is it?

He opens the door and Alex falls forward to the floor.

Alex: Help . . . please . . . help . . . help.

Julian: Frank, I think this young man needs some help.

Mr. Alexander: My God!

What's happened to you, my boy?

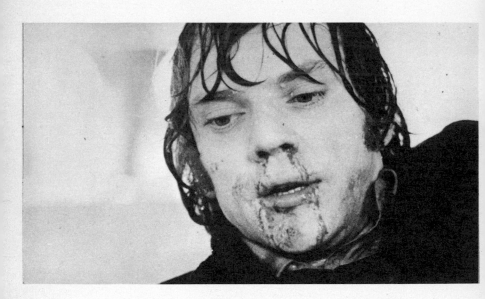

Alex: *(Voice Over)* **And would you believe it, O my brothers and only friends there was your Faithful Narrator being held helpless, like a babe in arms,**

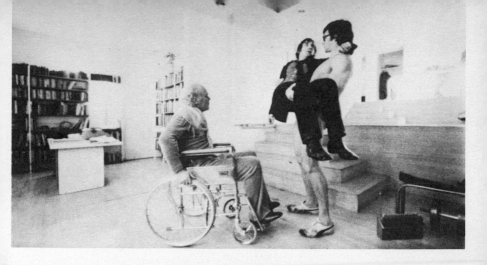

and suddenly realising where he was and
why "Home" on the gate had looked so
familiar.

But I knew I was safe. I knew he
would not remember me. For in those
carefree days, I and my so-called droogs
wore our maskies, which were like real
horrorshow disguises.

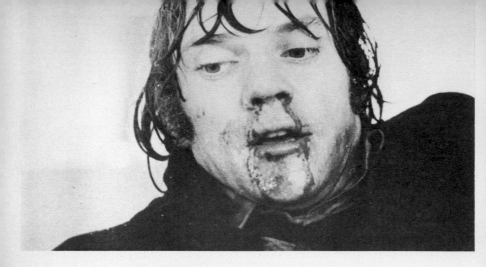

Alex: Police . . .

ghastly horrible Police . . .
they beat me up, sir. The Police beat me up, sir.
Mr. Alexander: I know you!

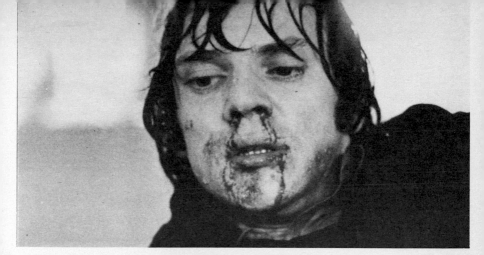

Isn't it your
picture in the newspapers? Didn't I see you on
the video this morning? Are you not the poor
victim of this horrible new technique?
Alex: Yes, sir! That's exactly who I am and
what I am, sir! A victim, sir!
Mr. Alexander: Then, by God, you have
been sent here by Providence! Tortured in
prison, then thrown out to be tortured by the
Police. My heart goes out to you, poor, poor
boy. Oh, you are not the first to come here in

distress. The Police are fond of bringing their victims to the outskirts of this village. But it is providential that you, who are also another kind of victim, should come here. Oh, but you're cold and shivering. Julian, draw a bath for this young man.

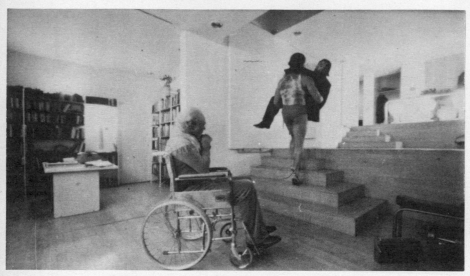

Julian: Certainly, Frank.
Alex: Thank you very much, sir.

God bless you, sir.

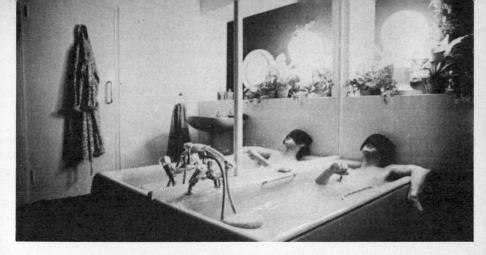

Night. Interior. Bathroom. Alex soaks in the tub. Starts to hum "Singin' in the Rain" which can be faintly heard behind the dialogue of the following scene.

Mr. Alexander: He can be the most potent weapon imaginable to ensure that the Government is not returned in the forthcoming election. The Government's big boast as you know, sir, is the way they have dealt with crime during the past few months. Recruiting brutal young roughs into the police, proposing debilitating and will-sapping techniques of conditioning. Oh, we've seen it all before in other countries. The thin end of the wedge. Before we know where we are we shall have the full apparatus of totalitarianism. This young boy is a living witness to these diabolical proposals. The people – the common people – must know . . . must see. There are great traditions of liberty to defend. The tradition of liberty is all. The common people will let it go. They will sell liberty for a quieter life – that is why they must be led, sir, driven, pushed ! ! ! Fine. . . Thank you very much, sir . . . He'll be here.

After he hangs up the telephone. Mr. Alexander slowly becomes aware of the song coming from the bathroom. He listens for a few seconds – then the penny drops. He wheels himself to the bathroom and puts his ear to the door.

Alex: *I'm singin' in the rain,*
                  Just singin' in the rain.
                  What a glorious feeling,
                  I'm hap . . hap . . happy again.
                  I'm laughing at clouds,
                  So dark up above.

The sun's in my heart,
And I'm ready for love.

Let the stormy clouds chase,
Everyone from the place.
Come on with the rain,
I've a smile on my face.

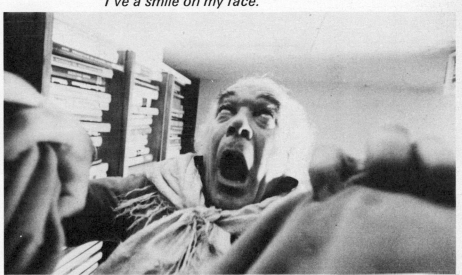

I'll walk down the lane
With a happy refrain,
And I'm singin', just singin'
in the rain.

Reel 14

Night. Interior. "Home".

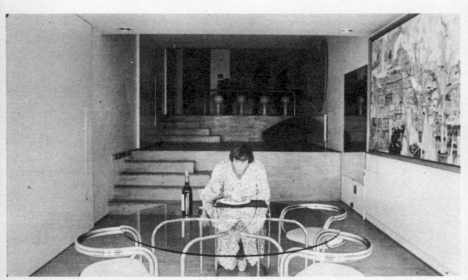

Mr. Alexander enters, carried in a wheelchair by Julian.

Alex: Good evening, sir.

Mr. Alexander: *(Voice trembling)* Good evening.

Alex: It was very kind of you, sir, to leave this out for me. There was no-one around when I finished my bath, so I started. I hope that's all right, sir.

Mr. Alexander: *(voice out of control)* Of course!!!

Alex smiles nervously and resumes eating in silence.

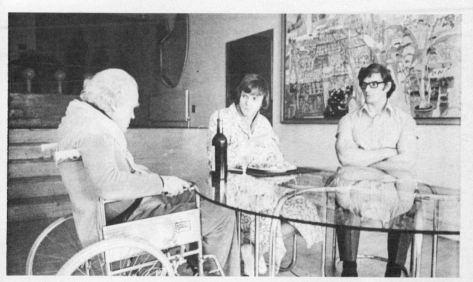

Food alright ? ? ? ?
Alex: Great, sir, great.
Mr. Alexander: *Try* the wine!!!!

Alex: Thank you, sir.
Cheers. Happy days.
*The idea occurs to Alex that there might be
something in the wine.*

Won't you join me?
Mr. Alexander: *No,* my health doesn't
allow it.
Julian: No, thank you.
Alex: 1960 Chateau, Saint Estephe, Medoc,
very good brand, sir.

Very good colour, sir. Smells nice, too.

He tastes it apprehensively.
Very nice little number, sir.
Well, here's to it.
He downs the glass
Very refreshing, sir, very refreshing.

Mr. Alexander: I'm pleased you appreciate
good wine. Have another *glass.*

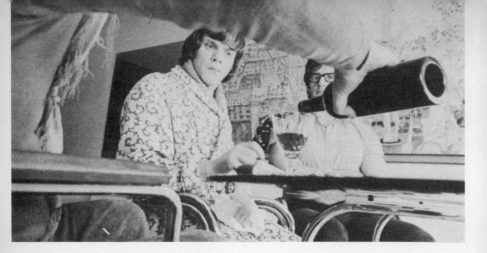

Alex: Thank you, sir.

Mr. Alexander: My *wife (trembles)* . . .

used to do everything for me, and leave me to
my writing.

Alex: Your wife, sir, is she away?

Mr. Alexander: *No*, she's *dead*. !!

Alex: I'm sorry to hear about that, sir.

Mr. Alexander: She was very badly raped, you see, We were assaulted by a gang of vicious young hoodlums in this house, in this very room you are sitting in now. I was left a helpless cripple, but for her the agony was too great. The doctors said it was pneumonia because it happened some months later during a 'flu epidemic. The doctors told me it was pneumonia but I knew what it was. A victim of the modern age—poor, poor girl.
He wheels closer to Alex.

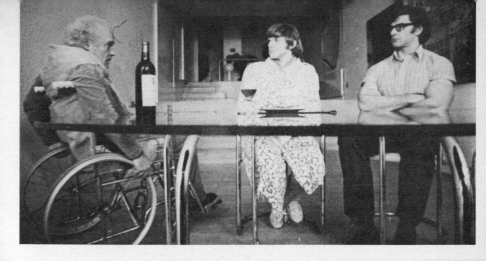

And now, *you*, another victim of the modern age,
but you can be helped.

I 'phoned some friends while
you were having your bath.
Alex: Some friends, sir?
Mr. Alexander: Yes, they want to help you.
Alex: Help *me*, sir?
Mr. Alexander: Help you.
Alex: Who are they, sir?
Mr. Alexander: They're very important
people, and they're interested in you.

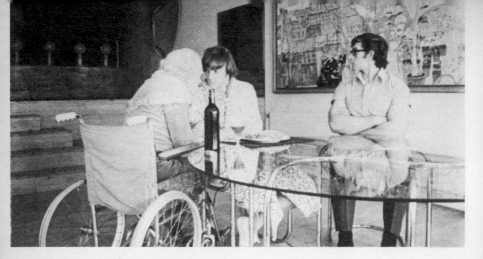

Door chimes.

Julian, this'll be these people now.
Alex: I don't think I want to trouble you any further, sir. I think I should be leaving.
Mr. Alexander: No, no, no, my boy. No trouble at all. Here, let me fill your glass.

Enter Rubinstein and Dolin.

Dolin: Hullo, Frank.

Mr. Alexander: Good evening, sir.

Rubinstein: *(kisses him on cheek)* Oh, Frank.

Dolin: So this is the young man.

Alex: How do you do, sir.

Dolin: Hullo.

Alex: Missus. Very pleased to meet you.

Rubinstein: Hello.

Dolin: I hope you'll forgive us for coming over at this ungodly hour, but we heard from Frank that you were in some trouble, and so we came over to see if we could be of any help.

Alex: Very kind of you, sir. Thank you very much.

Dolin: I understand that you had a rather unfortunate encounter with the police tonight?

Alex: Yes, sir, I suppose you could call it that, sir.

Dolin: How are you feeling now?
Alex: Much better, thank you, sir.
Dolin: Feel like talking to us, answering a few questions?
Alex: Fine, sir, fine.

Dolin: Well, as I've said, we've heard about you. We are interested in your case.

We want to help you.
Alex: Thank you very much, sir.

Dolin: Well, shall we get down to it?
Alex: Fine, fine, sir.

Rubinstein: The newspapers mentioned that, in addition to your being conditioned against acts of sex and violence, you've inadvertently been conditioned against music.

Alex: Well, I think that was something that they didn't plan for. You see, missus, I'm very fond of music, especially Beethoven . . . Ludwig van . . . Beethoven . . . B . . . E . . . . E . . .

Rubinstein: It's all right, thank you.

Alex: And it just so happened that while they were showing me a particularly bad film of, like, a concentration camp, the background music was playing Beethoven.

Rubinstein: So now you have the same reaction to music as you do to sex and violence?

Alex: No, missus, you see, it's not all music. It's just the Ninth.

Rubinstein: You mean, Beethoven's Ninth Symphony?

Alex: That's right. I can't listen to the Ninth any more at all. When I hear the Ninth, I get like this funny feeling

and then . . . all I can think
about is like trying to snuff it.

Rubinstein: I beg your pardon ?
Alex: Snuff it, sir . . . um . . . death, I mean,
missus . . . I just want to die peacefully, like,
with no pain.
Dolin: Do you feel that way now ?
Alex: Oh no, sir, not exactly. I still feel

very miserable, very much down in spirits.

Rubinstein: Do you still feel suicidal?
Alex: Well, put it this way. I feel very low in myself. I can't see much in the future and I feel that any second something terrible is going to happen to me.

*The drugged wine suddenly takes effect and
Alex suddenly falls forward into the plate of spaghetti.*

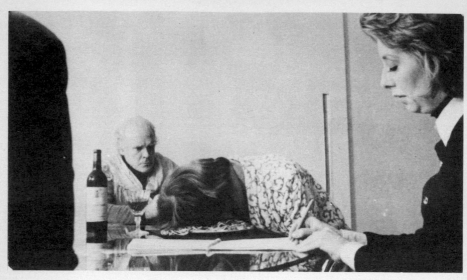

Mr. Alexander raises him up by the hair.

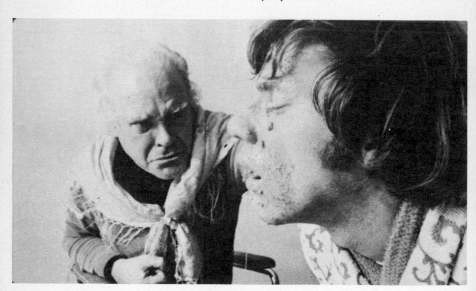

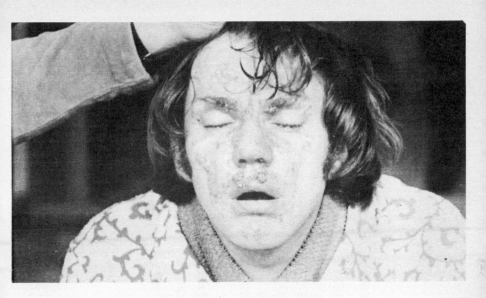

Dolin: Well done, Frank.

He lets Alex's head fall forward into the spaghetti.

Reel 15

Dolin: Julian, get the car would you please?

Alex: *(Voice Over)* I woke up. The pain
and sickness all over me like an animal.

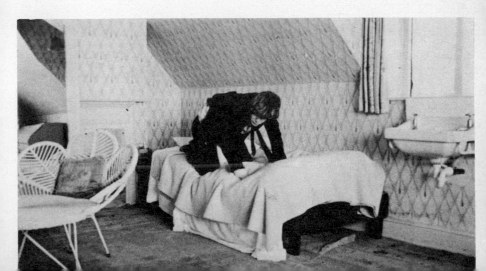

Then I realised what it was. The music coming up from the floor was our old friend, Ludwig van, and the dreaded Ninth Symphony.

Alex: Let me out!! Open the door!!! Come on, open the door!

He kicks and bangs.

Turn it off!!! Turn it off!!! Turn it off!!! Turn it off!!! Turn it off!!! Stop it . . .

Turn it off!!! Turn it off!!! Turn it off !!!

Turn it off!!! Please!!! Turn it off!!!

Alex: *(Voice Over)* **Suddenly, I viddied what I had to do, and what I had wanted to do, and that was to do myself in; to**

snuff it, to blast off for ever out of this wicked, cruel world.

One moment of pain perhaps and, then, sleep for ever, and ever and ever.

He jumps.

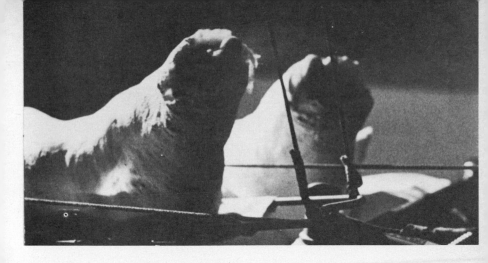

Night. Interior. Hospital ward.

Alex: (*Voice over*) I jumped, O my brothers, and I fell hard, but I did not snuff it. If I had snuffed it, I would not be here to tell what I have told. I came back to life, after a long black, black gap of what might have been a million years.

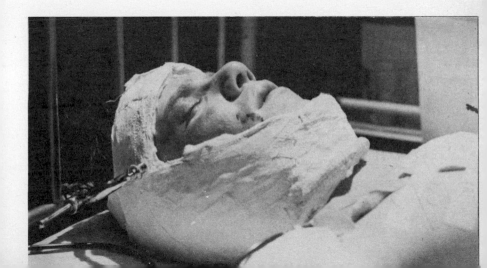

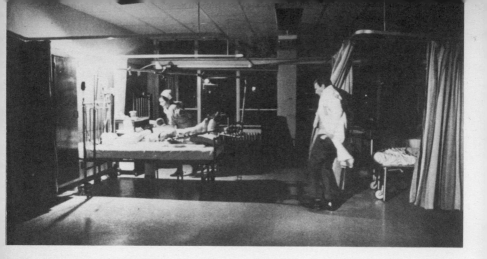

Nurse: Oh, he's recovered consciousness, Doctor.

BRAINWAS
ponsible f
Burgess, the "
released from

So say docto
when his body w
this week.

INVENT

M
of
'pois
wate
growi

THE TIM

NO. 63,485 NINEPENCE
[ONE SHILLING IN EIRE]

Government accused
of inhuman means
in crime reform

Accusations that scientific experiments, designed to reform convicted criminals, have directly contributed to the suicide attempt of a youth just released from prison, were made last night.

Doctors and MPs were blaming the so-called 'Ludovico Technique' for the mental pressures that caused one

of the first of its subjects to try and kill himself two days ago.

Our Political Staff says the Government is suffering acute embarrassment since these charges of inhuman experiments are bound to call into question the whole policy of law and order which it has made a plank in its election programme.

Author's
last

Boy attempts suicide

---

9 a.m.-8 p.m.   45,230

'Alex driven to suicide by scientists'

MINISTER IS
ACCUSED OF
INHUMAN CURE

By BERNARD CLEGG.

'GOVERNMENT IS MURDERER'

Doctors charge as Alex recovers

FRANK BECK

BRAINWASHING techniques were responsible for the suicide bid of Alex Burgess, the "wonder-cure" boy murderer released from jail only a few days ago.

So say doctors

STORM OVER
'CRIME CURE' BOY

Doctors blame government scientists for 'changing Alex's nature'

By LOUIS CARAS
Mirror Political Editor

DOCTORS last night blamed secret laboratory experiments on criminals for causing Alex Burgess, the 'Cat-Woman Killer,' to attempt suicide.

Alex's body was found on Wednesday just two days after he had been released from jail, a "cured" man. He had undergone the Ludovico Technique.

Spr

Blac
witch

Jonathan M
new King L

ahead fo
homes

ONS!

Alex's death bid blamed on brain men

Comment
Give us all the facts

Minister
under attack

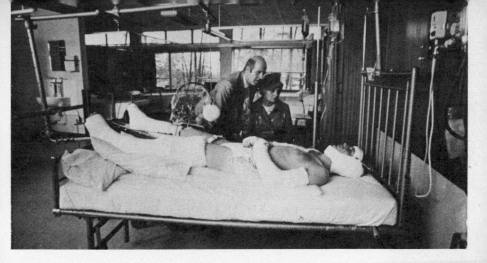

Day. Interior. Hospital Ward:

Pee: Hello, lad.
Em: Hello, son. How are you ?
Pee: Are you feeling better ?

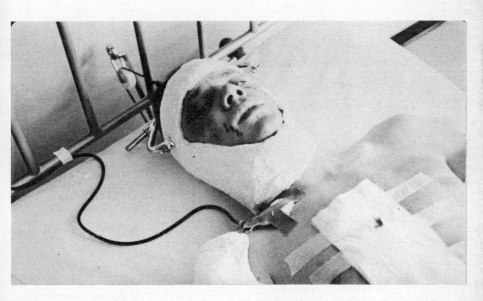

Alex: What gives, oh my Pee and Em,

what makes

you think you are welcome?

Em starts to cry.

Pee: There, there, mother, it's all right. He doesn't mean it. You were in the papers again, son. It said they had done great wrong to you. It said how the Government drove you to try and do yourself in . And when you think about it, son, maybe it was our fault too, in a way . _ Your home's your home when all's said and done, son.

Day. Interior. Hospital ward.

Psychiatrist enters.

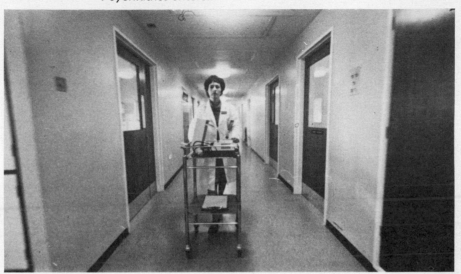

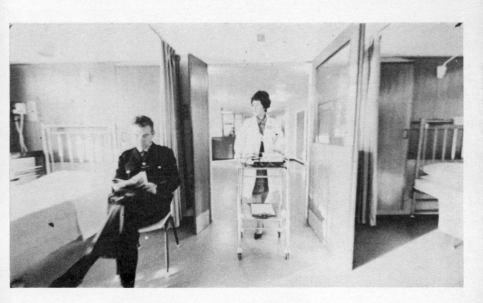

Dr. Taylor: Good morning.
Officer: Good morning, doctor.

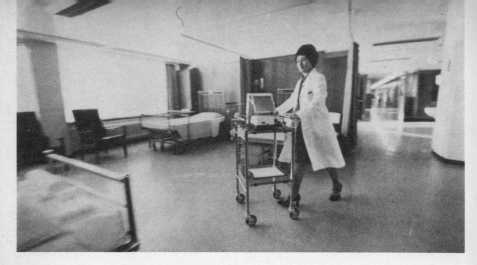

Walks to bed.

Dr. Taylor: Good morning.
Alex: Good morning, missus.
Dr. Taylor: How are you feeling today?
Alex: Fine, fine.

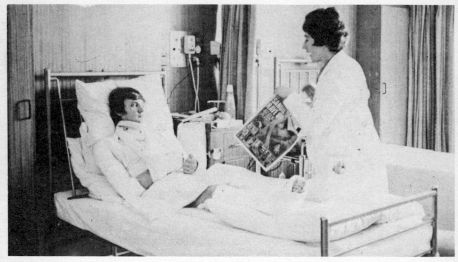

Dr. Taylor: Good. May I? I'm Doctor Taylor.
Alex: Haven't seen you before.
Dr. Taylor: I'm your psychiatrist.
Alex: Psychiatrist? Do I need one?
Dr. Taylor: Just part of hospital routine.
Alex: What are we going to do, talk about me sex life?

Dr. Taylor: Oh no, I'm going to show you some slides and you are going to tell me what you think about them. Alright?

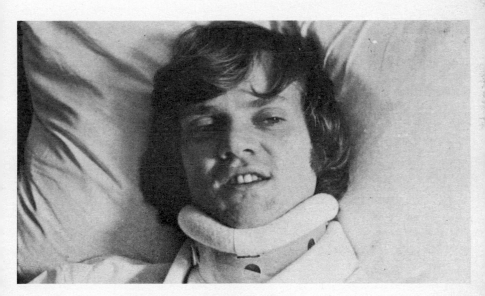

Alex: Oh, jolly good.

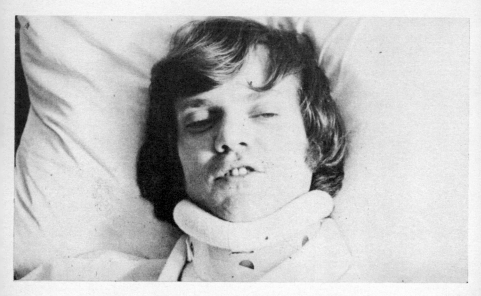

Do you know anything about dreams?

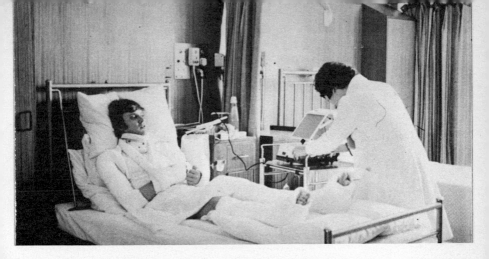

Dr. Taylor: Something, yes.
Alex: Do you know what they mean?
Dr. Taylor: Perhaps. Are you concerned about something?

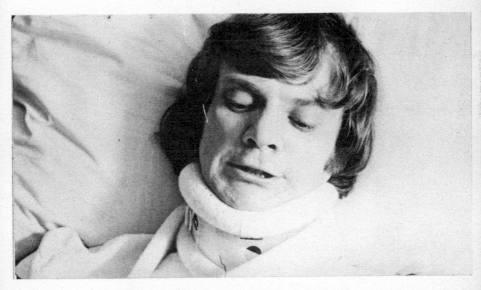

Alex: No, no, not concerned really, but I've been having this very nasty dream, very nasty.

It's like well, when I was all

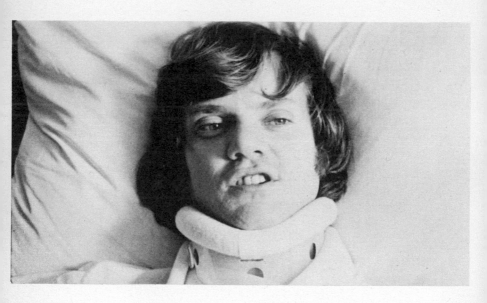

smashed up, you know, and half awake and
unconscious like, I kept having this dream. Well, like
all these doctors were playing around with my
gulliver, you know, like the inside of my brain.
I seemed to have this dream

over and over again. Do you think
it means anything ?
Dr. Taylor: Patients who have sustained
the kind of injuries you have often have
dreams of this sort. It's all part of the recovery
process.

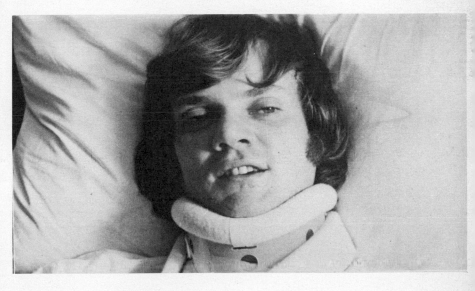

Alex: Oh.

Dr. Taylor: Now then, each of these slides needs a reply from one of the people in the picture. You tell me what you think the person would say. Alright?

Alex: Righty, right.

Dr. Taylor: Isn't the plumage beautiful?

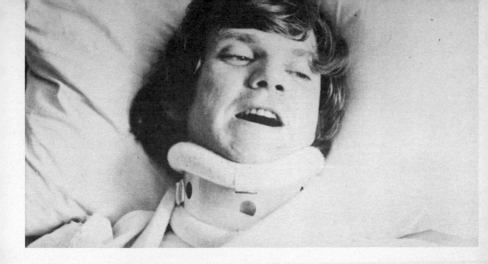

Alex: I just say what the other person would say?
Dr. Taylor: Yes.
Alex: Yes. Isn't the plumage beautiful . . .

Dr. Taylor: Oh, yes, well, don't think about it too long. Just say the first thing that pops into your mind.

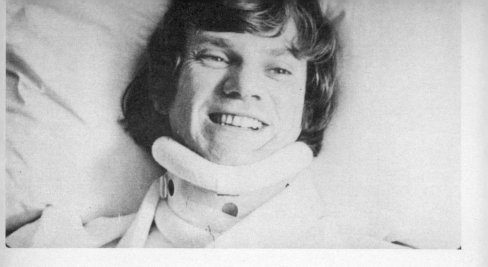

Alex: Cabbages . . . Knickers . . . It's not got a beak.

Dr. Taylor: Good.

Alex laughs

The boy you always quarrelled with

is seriously ill.

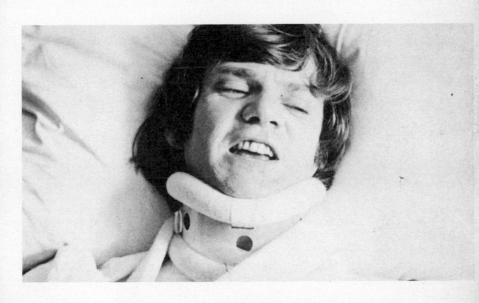

Alex: My mind is a blank. Uh-hhh. The boy . .
And I'll smash your face for you, yarblockos.
Dr. Taylor: Good.

More laughter

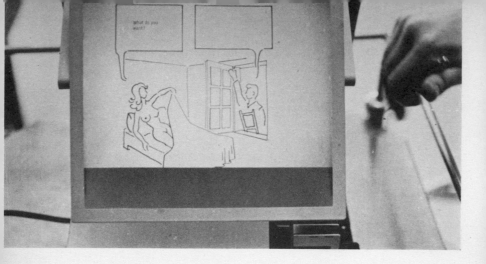

What do you want?

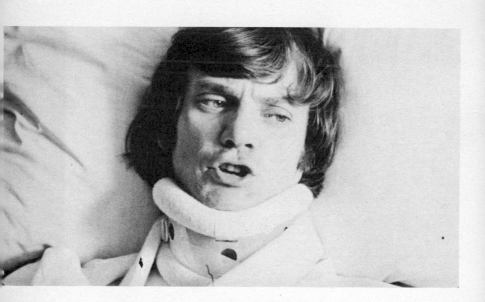

Alex: No time for the old in-out, love. I've just come to read the meter.

Dr. Taylor: Good.

You sold me a crummy watch.
I want my money back.

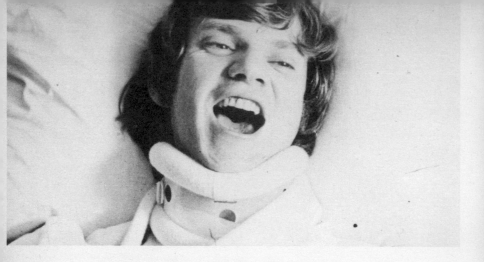

Alex: Do you know what you can do with that watch ? – Stick it up your arse.
Dr. Taylor: Good.

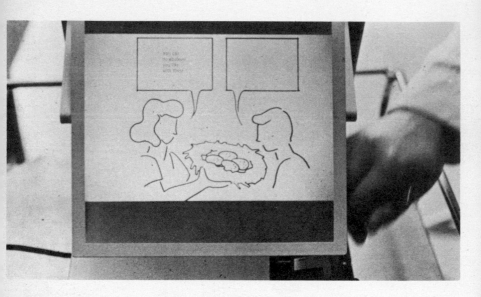

You can do whatever you like with these.

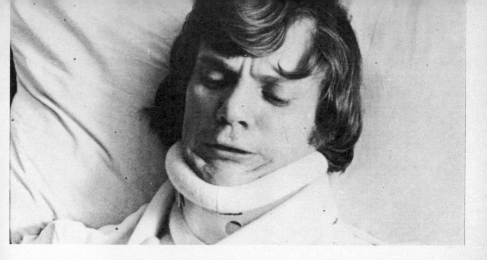

Alex: Eggiwegs . . . I would like to smash 'em, and pick 'em all up, and . . . owww.

Alex slams his broken hand down and curses in pain.

Fucking hell!

Dr. Taylor: Well, there, that's all there is to

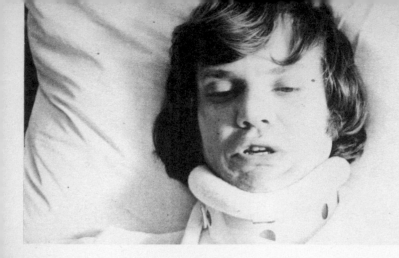

Are you alright?
Alex: Hope so. Is that the end, then?
Dr. Taylor: Yes.
Alex: Oh, I was quite enjoying that.

Dr. Taylor: Good, I'm glad.

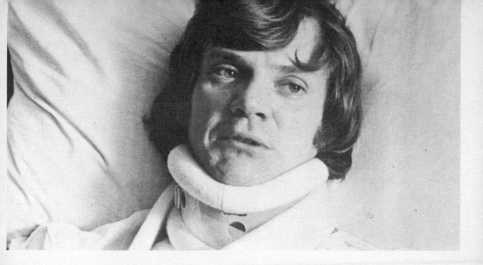

Alex: How many did I get right?

Dr. Taylor: Oh, it's not that kind of a
test but you seem well on the way to making
a complete recovery.

Alex: When do I get out of here, then?
Dr. Taylor: I'm sure it won't be long now.

Alex in bed being fed by nurse.

Alex: (*Voice over*) So I waited and, O
my brothers,

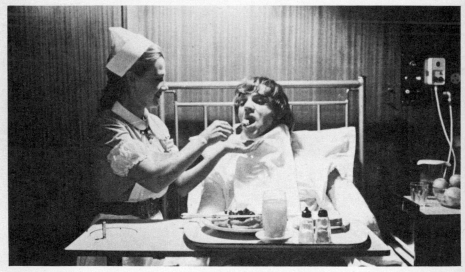

I got a lot better munching
away at eggiwegs, and lomticks of toast·
and lovely steakiweaks and then, one day,
they said I was going to have a very
special visitor.

Reel 16

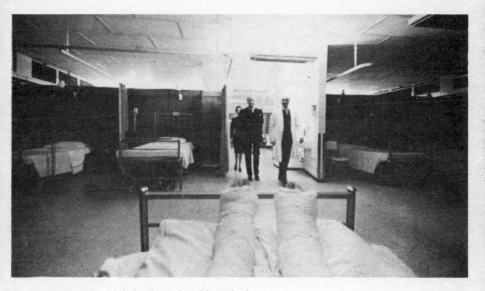

Night. Interior. Hospital

Doctor: Just wait outside for a moment, would you, Officer?

Officer: Yes, sir.

Minister: I'm afraid my change of schedule has rather thrown you. I seem to have arrived when the patients are in the middle of supper.

Doctor: It's quite alright, Minister. No trouble at all.

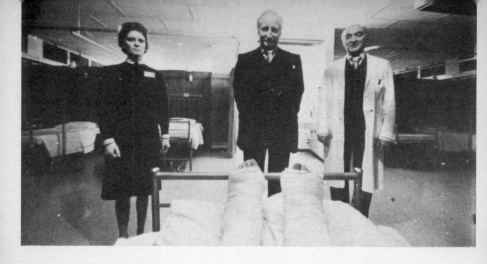

Minister: Good evening, my boy.
Alex: Hi, hi, hi, there, my little droogies.
Doctor: Well, how are you getting on today, young man?

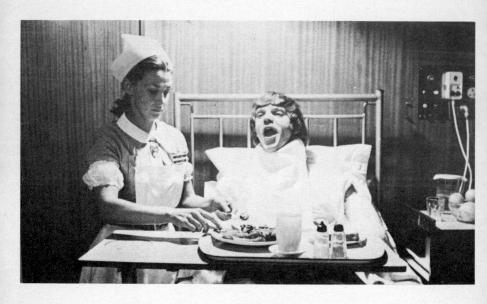

Alex: Great, sir, just great.

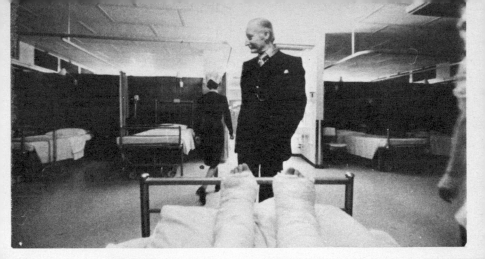

Doctor: Can I do anything more for you, Minister?
Minister: I don't think so, Sir Leslie, thank you very much.
Doctor: Then I'll leave you to it. Nurse.
They exit.

Minister: Well, you seem to have a whole ward to yourself, my boy.

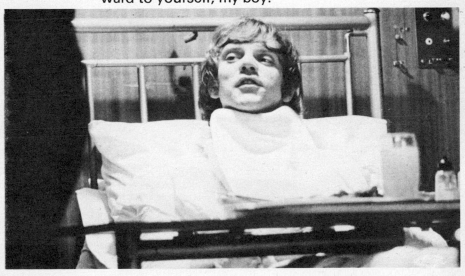

Alex: Yes, sir, and a very lonely place it is too, sir, when I wake up in the middle of the night with my pain.

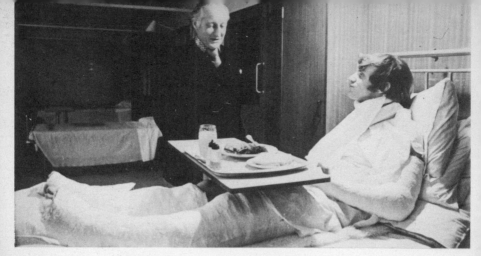

Minister: Yes . . . well, anyway, good to see you on the mend. I've kept in constant touch with the hospital, of course, and now I've come down to see you personally, to see how you're getting along.

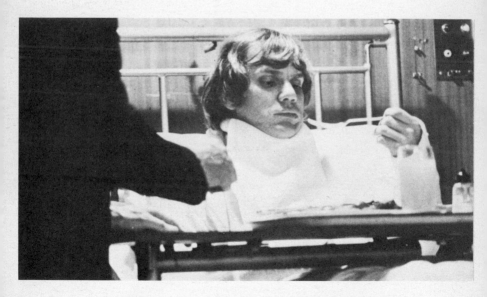

Alex: I've suffered the tortures of the damned, sir. . . . tortures of the damned.
Minister: Yes, I can appreciate that you have had an extremely . . .
Clumsily trying to feed himself, Alex drops peas on his lap.

Oh . . . look, let me help you with that, shall I ?

Minister feeds Alex.

Alex: Thank you, sir, thank you.
Minister: I can tell you with all sincerity
that I, and the Government of which I am a
member, are deeply sorry about this, my boy,
deeply sorry. We tried to help you. We
followed recommendations

which were made to us that turned out to be wrong.
An enquiry will place the responsibility

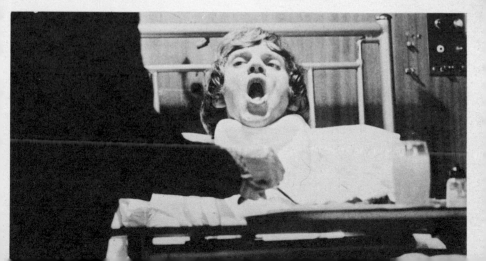

where it belongs. We want you to regard
us as friends. We put you right.

You are getting the best of treatment.
We never wished you harm, but there are some
who did, and do,

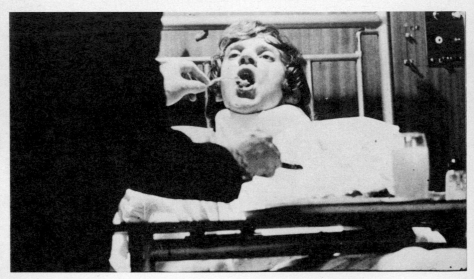

and I think you know who those are.
There are certain people who wanted
to use you for

political ends. They would have
been glad to have you dead, for they thought
they could then blame it all on the Government.

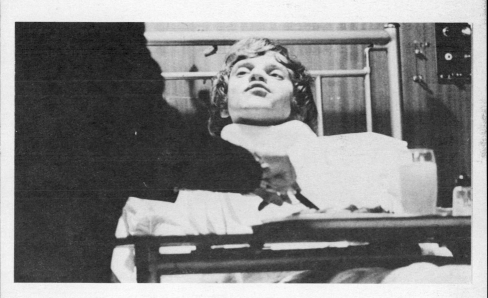

There is also a certain

man, a writer of subversive literature,
who has been howling for your blood.
He has been mad with desire to stick
a knife into you but you are safe

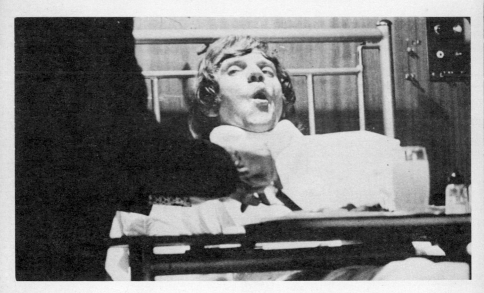

from him now. We put him away.
He found out that you had done wrong to him.

At least he believed you had done wrong.
He formed this idea in his head that you had
been responsible for the death of someone
near and dear to him.

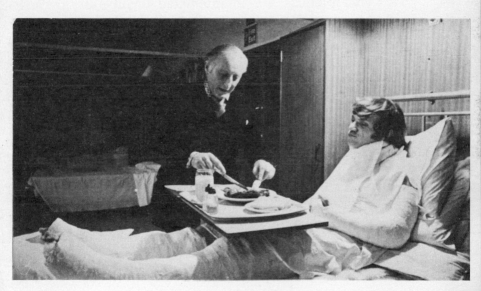

He was a menace. We put him away for his
own protection . . . and also for yours.

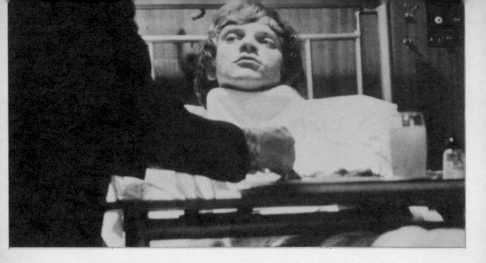

Alex: Where is he now, sir?
Minister: We put him away where he can do you no harm. You see, we are looking after your interests. We are interested in you and

when you leave here you will have no worries. We shall see to everything – a good job

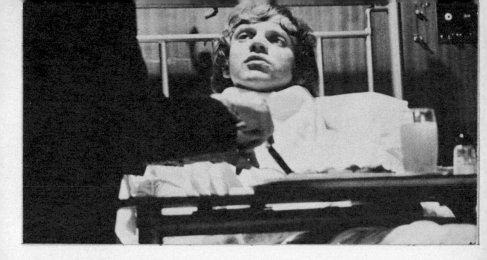

on a good salary.
Alex: What job and how much?

Minister: You must have an interesting job at a salary which you would regard as adequate, not only for the job that you are going to do, and in compensation for what you believe you have suffered, but also because you are helping us.

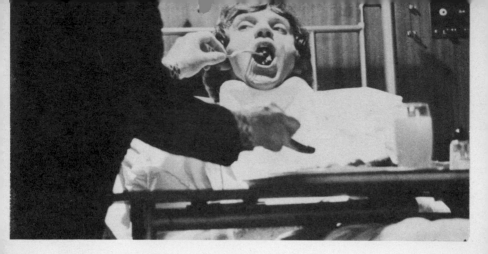

Alex: Helping you, sir?
Minister: We always help our friends, don't we? It is no secret that this Government has

lost a lot of popularity because of you, my boy. There are some who think that at the next election, we shall be out. The press has chosen to take a very unfavourable view of what we tried to do.

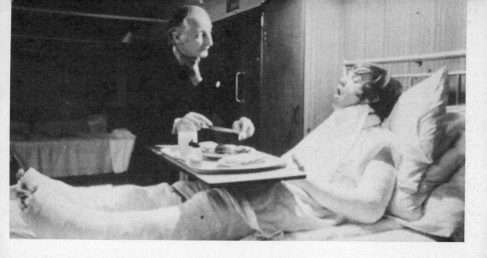

But public opinion has a way of
changing, and you, Alex, if I may call you
Alex ?
Alex: Certainly, sir. What do they call you at
home ?
Minister: My name is Frederick.

As I was saying, Alex, you can be
instrumental in changing the public's verdict.

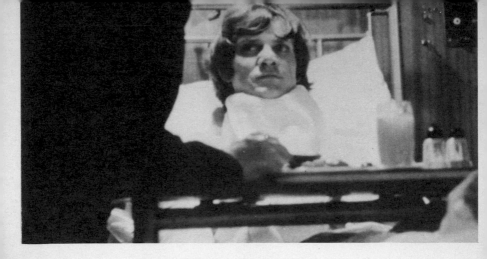

Do you understand, Alex?

Do I make myself clear?

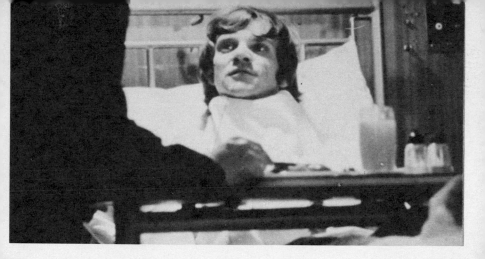

Alex: As an unmuddied lake, Fred. As clear as an azure sky of deepest summer. You can rely on me, Fred.

Minister: Good, good boy. Oh, yes, I understand you are fond of music. I have arranged a little surprise for you.

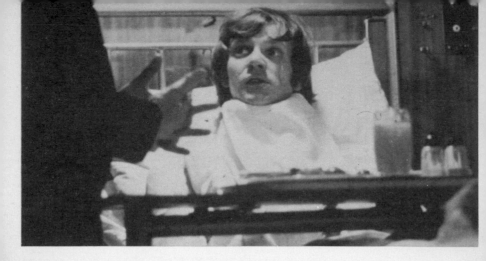

Alex: Surprise?
Minister: One that I think you will like . . .
as a . . .

how shall we put it . . . as a symbol of
our new understanding, an understanding
between two friends.

*Arrival of Press and Hi-Fi playing Beethoven's Ninth
Symphony.*

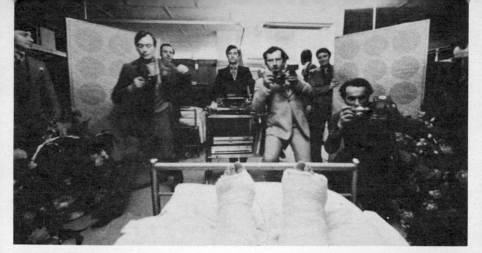

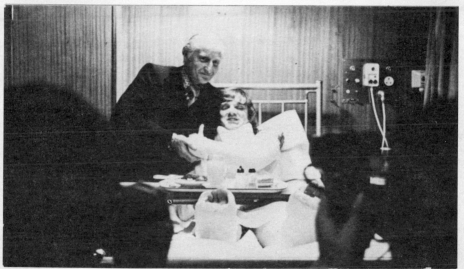

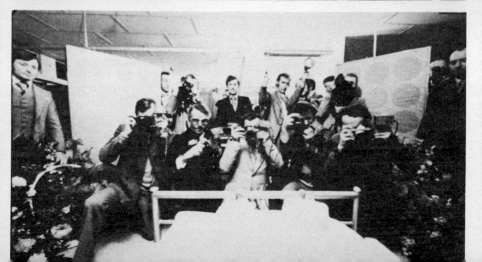

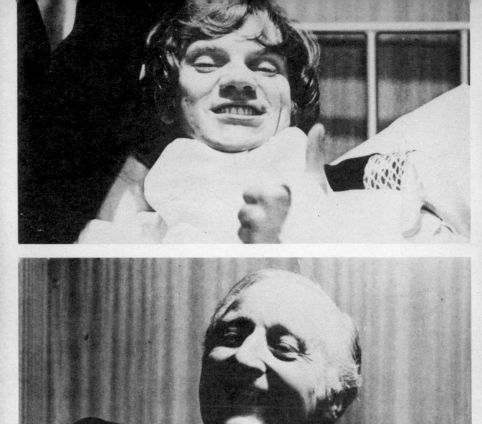

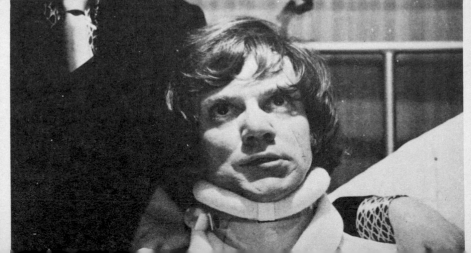

Alex: *(Voice Over)* I was cured all right.

Produced and Directed
by
STANLEY KUBRICK

Screenplay by
STANLEY KUBRICK

Based on the Novel by
ANTHONY BURGESS

STARRING

Alex
MALCOLM McDOWELL

Mr Alexander

PATRICK MAGEE

And
Featuring
In
Alphabetical
Order

Chief Guard

MICHAEL BATES

Dim

WARREN CLARKE

Stage Actor

JOHN CLIVE

Mrs. Alexander

ADRIENNE CORRI

Dr. Brodsky

CARL DUERING

Tramp

PAUL FARRELL

Lodger

CLIVE FRANCIS

Prison Governor
MICHAEL GOVER

Catlady
MIRIAM KARLIN

Georgie
JAMES MARCUS

Deltoid

AUBREY MORRIS

Prison Chaplain

GODFREY QUIGLEY

Mum

SHEILA RAYNOR

Dr. Branom
MADGE RYAN

Conspirator
JOHN SAVIDENT

Minister
ANTHONY SHARP

Dad
PHILIP STONE

Psychiatrist
PAULINE TAYLOR

Conspirator
MARGARET TYZACK

Executive Producers

MAX L. RAAB
and
SI LITVINOFF

Consultant on Hair and Coloring

LEONARD OF LONDON

Associate Producer

BERNARD WILLIAMS

Assistant to the Producer

JAN HARLAN

Electronic Music

Composed and Realised

by

WALTER CARLOS

Symphony No.9 in D Minor, Opus 125 by

LUDWIG VAN BEETHOVEN

Overtures "The Thieving Magpie" and "William Tell" by

GIOACHINO ROSSINI

Recorded by

DEUTSCHE GRAMMOPHON
GESELLSCHAFT

Pomp and Circumstance Marches No.1 and 4 by

EDWARD ELGAR

Conducted by MARCUS DODS

"Singin' in the Rain" by

ARTHUR FREED
and
NACIO HERB BROWN

From the MGM Picture

Performed by

GENE KELLY

"Overture to the Sun" Composed by

TERRY TUCKER

Song
"I Want to Marry a Lighthouse Keeper"
composed and performed by

ERIKA EIGEN

Lighting Cameraman

JOHN ALCOTT

Production Designer

JOHN BARRY

Editor

BILL BUTLER

Sound Editor

BRIAN BLAMEY

Sound Recordist

JOHN JORDAN

Dubbing Mixers

BILL ROWE
EDDIE HABEN

ART DIRECTORS	RUSSELL HAGG
	PETER SHEILDS
WARDROBE SUPERVISOR	RON BECK
COSTUME DESIGNER	MILENA CANONERO
STUNT ARRANGER	ROY SCAMMELL

Special Paintings and Sculpture

HERMAN MAKKINK
CORNELIUS MAKKINK
LIZ MOORE
CHRISTIANE KUBRICK

CASTING	JIMMY LIGGAT
LOCATION MANAGER	TERENCE CLEGG
SUPERVISING ELECTRICIAN	FRANK WARDALE
ASSISTANT DIRECTORS	DEREK CRACKNELL
	DUSTY SYMONDS
CONSTRUCTION MANAGER	BILL WELCH
PROP MASTER	FRANK BRUTON
ASSISTANT EDITORS	GARY SHEPHERD
	PETER BURGESS
	DAVID BEESLEY

CAMERA OPERATORS	ERNIE DAY
	MIKE MOLLOY
FOCUS-PULLER	RON DRINKWATER
CAMERA ASSISTANTS	LAURIE FROST
	DAVID LENHAM
BOOM OPERATOR	PETER GLOSSOP
GRIPS	DON BUDGE
	TONY CRIDLIN
ELECTRICIANS	LOUIS BOGUE
	DEREK GATRELL
PROP MEN	PETER HANCOCK
	TOMMY IBBETSON
	JOHN OLIVER

PROMOTION CO-ORDINATOR	MIKE KAPLAN
PRODUCTION ACCOUNTANT	LEN BARNARD
CONTINUITY	JUNE RANDALL
HAIRDRESSER	OLGA ANGELINETTA
MAKE-UP	FRED WILLIAMSON
	GEORGE PARTLETON
	BARBARA DALY
PRODUCTION SECRETARY	LORETTA ORDEWER
DIRECTOR'S SECRETARY	KAY JOHNSON
PRODUCTION ASSISTANT	ANDROS EPAMINONDAS
LOCATION LIAISON	ARTHUR MORGAN
TECHNICAL ADVISOR	JON MARSHALL

WITH SPECIAL ACKNOWLEDGEMENT TO

BRAUN AG FRANKFURT
DOLBY LABORATORIES INC.
KONTAKT WERKSTAETTEN
RYMAN CONRAN LIMITED
STEINHEIMER LEUCHTENINDUSTRIE
TEMDE AG

This story, all names, characters and incidents portrayed in this
production are fictitious. No identification with actual persons,
living or dead, is intended or should be inferred.

APPROVED   №º 22962

MOTION PICTURE ASSOCIATION OF AMERICA

THE END

Made at Pinewood Studios, London, England,
at EMI-MGM Studios, Borehamwood, Herts., England
and on location in England by Hawk Films Limited.

Distributed by

WARNER BROS.

A KINNEY COMPANY